BRITISH
SEA FISHES
By Dr Frances Dipper

U NDERWATER WORLD PUBLICATIONS LTD

BRITISH

SEA FISHES
By Dr Frances Dipper

Cover picture: Red Gurnard, by Mark Deeble and Victoria Stone.

Book designed and edited by John Hall. Production by Suzanne Blyskal

Typset in Times by P&M Typesetting Ltd, Linacre House, Southernhay East, Exeter
EX1 1UG, and printed by W.S. Cowell Ltd., 8 Butter Market, Ipswich, Suffolk.

ISBN: 0 946020 13 2

OTHER books from Underwater World Publications: *Great British Wrecks (vols 1, 2 and 3)* by
Kendall McDonald; *Diving For All*, by Alan Watkinson; *Easy Diving*, by Lou Fead and Alan
Watkinson; *Blackford's Diving Life and Times*, by Andy Blackford; *Dive Sussex*, by Kendall
McDonald; *The Diver Guide to South Devon*, by Kendall McDonald; *Dive Dorset*, by John and
Vicki Hinchcliffe; *The Diver Guide to South Cornwall*, by Richard Larn; *Dive West Scotland*, by
Gordon Ridley; *Dive North-West Scotland*, by Gordon Ridley.

Contents

Preface

FISH have long held an interest and fascination for me, and once I had learned to snorkel and then to dive in the clear waters of the Isle of Man, I was at last able to see for myself the grace, beauty and variety of fish in our home waters. My main frustration in those early days was in not being able to identify what fish I had seen, since this rarely compared easily with the drawings and paintings in the then-available guides, even when these were excellently written. John and Gillian Lythgoe's *Fishes of the Sea* with its many colour plates, went a long way to solving the problem. However, much of the book is concerned not with our home waters, but with the Mediterranean. Alwynne Wheeler's *Key to the Fishes of Northern Europe* is also an indispensible and comprehensive guide, but is illustrated only with line drawings. I was therefore delighted to be asked by Bernard Eaton to write this book, and I sincerely hope that the colour photographs and simple text will allow any diver, snorkellor, fisherman or even schoolchild, to avoid the frustration I so often felt, and to identify easily the marine fish he or she will see around our varied coastline.

At this stage I would like to say although the book appears under the author's name, any credit due should go to all the underwater photographers, amateur and professional alike, who had the patience and skill to take such beautiful photographs, and who have so willingly supplied us with their photographs. Without their help this book would not exist. My thanks should also go to the illustrator, Robert Irving, himself a keen diver and underwater photographer, whose precise and clear drawings compliment the photographs so well. I am also indebted to Alwynne Wheeler of the British Museum (Natural History) for his advice and help. Finally, the patience of my three-year-old daughter, who so often helped me to type out the text, should not be forgotten.

Frances Dipper

Introduction

THIS BOOK is a field guide to the common sea fishes of Great Britain and Ireland. Since fish know no political or ethnic boundaries, the area covered includes England, Scotland, Wales, Northern Ireland, the Republic of Ireland, the Isle of Man, Orkney, Shetland and the Scilly Isles. The guide includes all the species likely to be seen by divers, snorkellors, visitors to the sea shore and inshore anglers. Fish restricted to deep water (below about 50m), open ocean species, very rare fish and casual summer visitors from warmer southern climes are mostly excluded. However, some of the latter two categories are covered in Section IV – rarely seen fish.

The main aim of the book is to allow easy and accurate identification of marine fish in their natural environment, or alive and freshly taken from it. In this respect it resembles an underwater version of a birdspotter's guide. These aims hopefully have been achieved by the use of colour photographs of nearly all the species covered, and taken almost entirely by amateur divers pursuing their hobby of underwater photography. In only a few cases has it been necessary to resort to aquarium photographs.

Most existing fish identification books rely on line drawings or paintings of (mostly dead) fish. Whilst a number of these are excellent reference books (see bibliography) such illustrations cannot convey the colour and appearance of the fish in its natural habitat. However, since most fish are not in the habit of posing under water to display all their salient features, a small drawing of each species is also included to highlight the key identification features.

The species in the book are not arranged in scientific, taxonomic order, but rather, according to where they are usually found in the wild – in other words under habitat headings. Section I covers fish that live in areas where the sea-bed is soft; that is, on, in and around sediments such as sand, mud, gravel or mixtures of these. Section II includes fish associated in some way with hard sea-beds; that is, on, in or around rocky areas, shipwrecks or other man-made artifacts. Section III covers fish that are not associated with any particular kind of sea-bed but instead spend most of their time in open water. Most of these species live in large groups – schools or shoals.

Since fish are highly mobile animals, they will on occasion be found outside their preferred habitat, or in areas of mixed habitat such as boulders and sand. Some species live equally happily in either sediment or rocky areas, and these have been included in the most convenient section. A final and fourth section covers a number of species that are genuinely rare or that are for some reason rarely seen. There are obviously a large number of fish that fall into this category, and the species included are those that are easily recognised and can be met on a fairly regular basis if the right areas and habitats are visited.

For each species or pair of species, the text is arranged under seven headings.

DESCRIPTION covers the characteristic features by which the fish can be identified. This includes colour, since one photograph cannot convey variations due to habitat, sex and time of year.

SIZE gives the approximate maximum total length (tip of snout to tip of tail). A usual or average length is also often given. Since most observers will not have the chance to measure the fish, a yardstick comparison in arm and hand lengths is usually given.

DISTRIBUTION AND HABITAT describes approximately where the species occurs around the British Isles. It does not indicate its distribution outside the United Kingdom. Finding a species outside its stated distributional limits may indicate either a mis-identification or an extension to the known range of the species. The usual habitat and depth limits for each species are also given.

BIOLOGY lists brief details of the life history, feeding habits, predators and commercial uses by man.

BEHAVIOUR describes aspects of the fish's natural behaviour in the wild, and also how it may react to divers. This can often provide a clue to the fish's identity.

SIMILAR SPECIES highlights possible areas of confusion, and in some cases mentions similar but rarely seen species not otherwise included in the book.

KEY IDENTIFICATION FEATURES lists the important identification features shown in the photographs and drawings.

How to use this book

TO IDENTIFY a completely unfamiliar fish, turn first to the identification key given on p.10. In this simple key, all the fish described in the book are divided into nine groups, based on their main body shape and how many dorsal fins they have. Having decided to which main group the fish belongs, turn to the relevant pages as given in the key.

Note that some species are included in two or more main groups. For example the butterfish (*Pholis gunnellus*) is an elongated fish (Group 2) and it has one dorsal fin (Group 4) so provided one or other of these two features is noticed, it will be possible to find the relevant pages. Remember when looking at the number of dorsal fins that the fish may be carrying these in a folded down position where they are not so easy to see.

A general description of all the families of fish covered in the book is given on pp.12–18, with outline drawings of the fish showing their general body form and shape. These pages should also help in initially deciding what sort of fish you have seen.

Identification key

GROUP 1. FLATTENED FISH USUALLY FOUND ON THE
SEA BED.
    Flatfish, 24–36, 86, 88.
    Rays, 38, 40, 176, 178.
    Angler fish, 42.
    Dragonets, 58.

GROUP 2. FISH WITH ELONGATED EEL-LIKE OR SNAKE-LIKE
BODIES.
    Viviparous blenny, 70.
    Yarrell's blenny, 108.
    Snake blenny, 82.
    Butterfish, 110.
    Pipefish, 72, 74, 114, 116.
    Red band fish, 76.
    Sticklebacks, 130.
    Garfish, 180.
    Eels, 118, 120.
    Ling, 122.
    Rocklings, 124.
    Wolf fish, 126.

GROUP 3. SHARK-LIKE FISH WITH THE MOUTH UNDER THE
HEAD, GILL SLITS AND NO SCALES.
    Dogfish, 44.
    Other small sharks, 46–50.
    Basking shark, 162.

GROUP 4. CLINGING FISH WITH PELVIC FINS MODIFIED AS A
SUCKER.
    Lumpsucker, 90.
    Sea-snails, 92.
    Clingfish, 94, 96.

GROUP 5. UNUSUALLY SHAPED FISH – IMMEDIATELY
RECOGNIZABLE.
    Lumpsucker, 90.
    John Dory, 146.
    Wolf fish, 174.
    Angler fish, 42.

General description of fish groups and families

Group numbers given in parentheses refer to the Identification Key (p. 10).

1. FLATFISH. Pleuronectidae, Soleidae,
Scophthalmidae, Bothidae.
(Group 1).

Bottom-living fish compressed from side to side and found mostly on sediments; topknots prefer rocks. When resting on the seabed, they lie either on their left or right side, and they have both eyes on the upward-facing side. Brill, turbot, topknots and scaldfish are left-eyed flatfish with the eyes on the left side. Plaice, flounder, dabs and soles are right-eyed. Look for position of mouth and visualise the fish upright to tell which side the eyes are on. Oval or round with a fringe of fins.
p.p. 24–36, 86–88.

2. RAYS. Rajidae, Torpedinidae, Dasyatidae,
Myliobatidae.
(Group 1).

Seabed fish flattened from top to bottom so that they lie belly down. Mostly on sediments, but some swim in open water. Larger species with long snouts are generally called skates, and smaller species with short snouts are called rays. There is no real biological distinction. Typically diamond-shaped with a long thin tail. Electric rays are rounded. Mouth and gill slits are hidden on the underside. Cartilaginous fish related to the sharks.
p.p. 38–40, 176–178.

3. ANGLER FISH. Lophiidae.
(Groups 1 & 5).

Bizarre-shaped fish, flattened from top to bottom with huge mouths. All have a "fishing lure" on the head to entice prey within reach of the capacious jaws.
p. 42.

4. SHARKS. Scyliorhinidae, Carcharinidae, Triakidae, Squalidae, Cetorhinidae.
(Group 3).

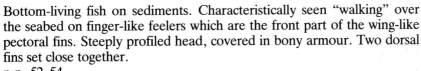

Includes dogfish, nursehound, tope, smooth hounds, spurdogs and basking shark. Sharks have a skeleton of cartilage, not bone, and so do not have spiny fins. The mouth is slung under the head; either side of the head is a series of gill slits (usually five). The tail is asymmetrical, with a long upper lobe. The skin is rough, and instead of scales, is covered in small, sharp, backward-pointing "teeth". Most sharks around Britain are small and harmless, but larger, potentially dangerous species, such as porbeagle, mako and thresher occur offshore, especially in summer.
p.p. 44–50, 162.

5. GURNARDS. Triglidae.
(Group 8).

Bottom-living fish on sediments. Characteristically seen "walking" over the seabed on finger-like feelers which are the front part of the wing-like pectoral fins. Steeply profiled head, covered in bony armour. Two dorsal fins set close together.
p.p. 52–54.

6. DRAGONETS. Callionymiidae.
(Groups 1 & 8).

Bottom-living fish on sediments. Head flattened and triangular when seen from above; body tapering. Two dorsal fins set close together, the first triangular and very high in males, but usually carried folded down. Females drab, sandy colour, males bright. Three species in British waters, but only one really common in inshore areas.
p. 58.

7. POGGES. Agonidae.
(Group 8.)

Small, bottom-living fish, mostly on sediments. Body heavily armoured, with bony, overlapping plates. Fringe of barbels around mouth. Two short dorsal fins. One species around Britain.
p. 56.

8. RED MULLET. Mullidae.
(Group 8).

Bottom-living fish on sediments. Move slowly over seabed, probing for food with two conspicuous, long, chin barbels. Head with steeply rounded profile. Two short dorsal fins. One species around Britain.
p. 60.

9. WEEVER FISH. Trachinidae.
(Group 8).

Bottom-living fish on sediments. Usually lie buried, with just head or eyes showing. Large head with oblique mouth, eyes set high up. Two dorsal fins, the first short, with very poisonous spines, the second long. Intensely painful if trodden on. Two species around Britain.
p. 78.

10. SEA SCORPIONS. Cottidae.
(Group 8).

Small, spiny, bottom-living fish, mostly on rocks. Also known as bullheads or sculpins. Stout body; broad spiny and knobbly head. Two nearly equal dorsal fins, the first sharply spiny. Colour varies according to habitat. Two common species; one other only found around north Scotland.
p. 112.

11. GOBIES. Gobiidae.
(Group 8).

Small, widespread, and abundant bottom-living fish on sediments and rocks. Identification difficult. Broad head, cylindrical body. Swollen cheeks, thick lips, eyes set high on head. Two dorsal fins. Pelvic fins joined to form a disc with weak adhesive powers. 18 species recorded around Britain, but only 7 are common.
p.p. 62–66, 98–100, 144, 182.

12. BLENNIES. Blennidae.
(Group 7).

Small, bottom-living fish, mostly on rocks in shallow water and on shore. Large, bulbous eyes, set high on head; thick lips. Single, long dorsal fin. Pelvic fins reduced to two long rays, often used to prop the fish up when resting on the bottom. Three of the four species around Britain have prominent tentacles on the head.
p.p. 68, 102–106.

13. BLENNY-LIKE FISH (ARCTIC BLENNIES AND EEL-POUTS). Pholidae, Stichaeidae, Zoarcidae.
(Groups 2 & 7).

Bottom-living fish resembling blennies, but with long, eel-like bodies. Single, long dorsal fin. Includes the butterfish, snake blennies, Yarrell's blenny and viviparous blenny (eel-pout). Only Yarrell's blenny has head tentacles.
p.p. 70, 82, 108–110.

14. PIPEFISH. Syngnathidae.
(Groups 2 & 7).

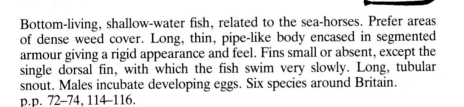

Bottom-living, shallow-water fish, related to the sea-horses. Prefer areas of dense weed cover. Long, thin, pipe-like body encased in segmented armour giving a rigid appearance and feel. Fins small or absent, except the single dorsal fin, with which the fish swim very slowly. Long, tubular snout. Males incubate developing eggs. Six species around Britain.
p.p. 72–74, 114–116.

15. STICKLEBACKS. Gasterosteidae.
(Group 2).

Small fish living in shallow, weed-covered areas in both salt and fresh waters. Long, torpedo-shaped body. Single dorsal fin preceded by a number of individual, sharp spines. A sharp spine in each pelvic fin. Males build elaborate nests and court females. Two species in seas around Britain; one more in fresh water.
p. 130.

16. CLINGFISH. Gobiesocidae.
(Groups 4 & 7).

Small, bottom-living fish, that cling to rocks and seaweeds with a powerful sucker formed by the modified pelvic fins. Rather flattened, with triangular-shaped heads. Eyes set high up. Single dorsal fin set near the tail. Four species around Britain, not easily identified.
p.p. 94–96.

17. LUMPSUCKER and SEA-SNAILS. Cyclopteridae.
(Groups 4, 5 & 7).

Stout, bottom-living fish, that cling mostly to rocks by a large, sucker-disc on the belly. Lumpsucker is distinctive, with hard plates and spines covering the body; two dorsal fins, but the first indistinguishable in adults. Sea-snails with loose, scaleless skin, and a single long dorsal fin.
p.p. 90–92.

18. EELS. Anguillidae, Congridae.
(Groups 2 & 7).

Bottom-living fish, usually hidden in crevices, holes, and amongst weeds. Long, slippery body, with one long dorsal fin that continues around the tail onto the belly. Adults make long spawning migrations, and have a complex life history, involving a transparent, leaf-shaped leptocephalus larva. Only conger and common eels in Britain's coastal waters.
p.p. 118–120.

19. ROCKLINGS and LING. Gadidae.
(Groups 2 & 8).

Bottom-living fish on rock and sediment, closely related to the cod. Ling elongated; rockling long, slippery, and eel-like. Rocklings have between 3–5 barbels on the snout; ling have a single chin barbel. Two dorsal fins, the first short and the second long. In rocklings the first is reduced to a fringe of short rays. The stouter-bodied tadpole fish also belong to this group.
p.p. 122–128.

20. COD-FISHES. Gadidae.
(Group 9).

Active swimming fish, mostly found in the vicinity of rocks and wrecks, but some also in large shoals in open water. Three soft dorsal fins and two anal fins. Most have a single chin barbel. This commercially important group includes cod, haddock, whiting, poor cod, bib, pollack and saithe. p.p. 148–158.

21. WRASSE. Labridae.
(Group 7).

Small to medium-sized fish, living in the vicinity of rocks and wrecks. Colourful, scaly fish. Mouth with thick lips and large teeth. Single, long dorsal fin, spiny at the front. Tail fin rounded. Swim by beating pectoral fins in characteristic rowing motion. Some change sex from female to male during their life. Five species around Britain, with another three species as rare visitors to the south coast.
p.p. 132–140.

22. SEA-BREAM. Sparidae.
(Group 7).

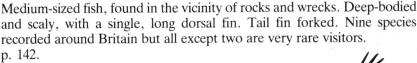

Medium-sized fish, found in the vicinity of rocks and wrecks. Deep-bodied and scaly, with a single, long dorsal fin. Tail fin forked. Nine species recorded around Britain but all except two are very rare visitors.
p. 142.

23. DORY. Zeidae.
(Group 5).

Distinctive, mostly solitary fish of both rocky and sandy inshore areas. Body very compressed sideways, and so hardly visible from head-on view. Large, protrusible mouth. One species around Britain.
p.146.

24. SEA BASS. Percichthyidae.
(Group 8).

Active, silvery, schooling fish, found mostly inshore around rocky reefs, and often in estuaries. Two dorsal fins set close together, the first spiny. One species around Britain.
p. 164.

25. GREY MULLET. Mugilidae.
(Group 8).

Active, silvery-grey schooling fish, found inshore, mostly over sediments and in estuaries. Torpedo-shaped, with characteristic grey, lengthwise stripes. Two short dorsal fins, the first spiny. Three very similar species around Britain.
p. 166.

26. MACKEREL. Scombridae.
(Group 8).

Active, schooling, open water fish. Spindle-shaped, streamlined body, designed for fast swimming. Two well separated dorsal fins, the second followed by a series of small finlets. Tail fin deeply forked. Most are a bluey-green on the back, whitish below. Nine species, including the closely related tunnies, recorded around Britain, but all except the common mackerel are rather rare summertime visitors from further south.
p. 168.

27. SCADS or HORSE MACKEREL. Carangidae.
(Group 8).

Active, schooling fish, resembling the mackerel but less streamlined. Row of large bony scales along the lateral line. Only one species common around Britain. Others are very rare visitors.
p. 168.

28. HERRINGS Clupeidae.
(Groups 6 & 7).

Silvery, schooling, open-water fish. Body slightly flattened from side to side; scales easily detached. Single, short dorsal fin, set near middle of back. Deeply forked tail fin. Six species around Britain, difficult to distinguish under water.
p.p. 170.

29. SAND EELS. Ammodytidae.
(Groups 6 & 7).

18

Small, silvery fish, usually seen in large shoals just above the sea-bed, but can disappear rapidly into the sand when frightened. Slender, with pointed snout and lower jaw sticking out. Single, long dorsal fin. Important source of food for other fish and sea-birds. Five species around Britain, only two living inshore.
p. 80.

30. WOLF-FISH. Anarhichidae.
(Groups 5, 2 & 7).

Bottom-living, mostly deep-water fish, related to and resembling blennies, apart from their much greater size. Long body with single, long dorsal fin. Large head with huge canine-like teeth visible, even when mouth closed. No pelvic fins.
p. 174.

31. GARFISH and SKIPPERS. Belonidae and Scomberesocidae.
(Group 2).

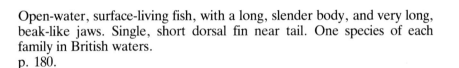

Open-water, surface-living fish, with a long, slender body, and very long, beak-like jaws. Single, short dorsal fin near tail. One species of each family in British waters.
p. 180.

32. RED BAND-FISH. Cepolidae.
(Groups 2 & 7).

Burrowing fish, found in mud. Long, slender, eel-like body, with single, long dorsal fin, continuous with tail and anal fins. Red colour. One species.
p. 76.

Parts of a fish

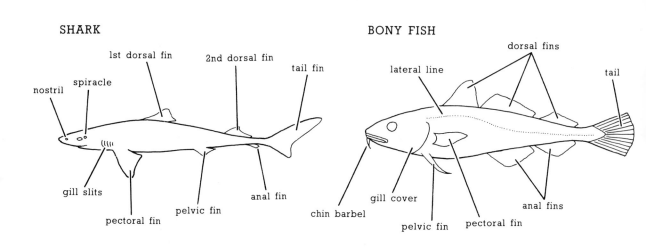

SHARK

1st dorsal fin
2nd dorsal fin
tail fin
spiracle
nostril
gill slits
pectoral fin
pelvic fin
anal fin

BONY FISH

dorsal fins
lateral line
tail
gill cover
chin barbel
pelvic fin
pectoral fin
anal fins

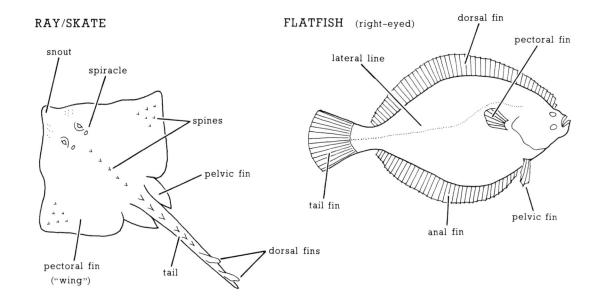

RAY/SKATE

snout
spiracle
spines
pelvic fin
pectoral fin
("wing")
tail
dorsal fins

FLATFISH (right-eyed)

dorsal fin
pectoral fin
lateral line
tail fin
anal fin
pelvic fin

Notes on the line drawings

THE majority of the drawings have been taken directly from the individual specimen photographs of the fish. Where there is no photograph, or where specific identification details are missing from the photograph, then the drawing has been made using information from other reference sources (see bibliography).

Where an identification feature is obvious, and requires no number on the drawing to indicate this, then the number has been omitted. This is also the case when habitats in which the fish is likely to be found are described.

In most cases, so as to avoid unnecessary confusion, fins are shown on one side of the body only.

If an appendage (i.e. fin, barbel, spines etc.) or body markings are not clearly shown in the photograph (either as a result of them being obscured or of them being excluded from the frame), then these have been added to the drawing, so that a complete picture of the fish is given.

Section I. Soft sea-beds or sediments (sand, mud and gravels)

FISH LIVING in these areas have two choices; they can either live on the surface of the sediment or they can burrow their way into it. Most prefer the first alternative, but almost all are able to bury lightly and thus conceal themselves. Fish in this section include flatfish, rays and skates, gurnards and similar fish, some gobies and blennies, pipefish, and true burrowing fish such as the red band fish. Also included are small sharks such as dogfish and tope, which although found predominantly on or over sediment bottoms, are also at home in rocky areas.

Sediment-living fish face three main problems. Firstly, unlike rocky areas with their cracks, crevices and often dense undergrowth, a flat sandy sea-bed provides little in the way of hidey holes. This means that sediment-living fish are constantly in danger of being eaten by larger predators, including other fish and seals. Secondly, although food in the form of shellfish, worms and crustaceans may be abundant, especially in the muddier sediments, it is usually buried, and must be found and dug out. The third problem is that sediments are inherently unstable and at the mercy of strong waves and tidal streams. This makes burrow construction difficult, except in sheltered or deep waters. The various fish that live in sediment areas have evolved a number of adaptations to overcome these problems.

By far the largest two groups of sediment-living fish are the flatfish and the rays or skates. Both groups have independently, and in different ways, adopted a flattened shape ideally suited to this habitat. By lying quietly on the sea-bed, often partly buried, they are well camouflaged from predators. Drab, sandy colours and a widespread ability to alter their colour patterns to suit the background, help with their camouflage. A further advantage is that food in the form of surface-living crustaceans, small fish etc will be unsuspecting and more easily snapped up. The angler fish has gone one step further and lures its prey towards its well-camouflaged jaws. Fish such as gurnards, pogges, and red mullet are able to search for buried food with sensory feelers and barbels located on or near the head, with which they can probe into the sediment.

With their small size and alert disposition, gobies and blennies thrive in sediment areas.

A few sediment-living fish can be classed as true burrowers. Some, like weever fish and sand eels, spend most or much of their time completely buried, but do not construct a proper burrow.

23

BRILL *Scophthalmus rhombus*

DESCRIPTION: The brill is a large flatfish with a broad body and wide fins, shaped rather like an oval dinner plate. The eyes are on the left side of the body. The front part of the dorsal fin appears rather untidy and frill-like because the first few rays are branched and partly free from the fin membrane. The skin has no bony tubercles and the lateral line is strongly arched over the pectoral fin. The fish can change its colour to suit the background but is basically brown, with numerous lighter and darker flecks and blotches giving it an overall spotty appearance.

SIZE: Brill usually grow up to 50cm long (length of arm without hand) but can reach 75cm.

DISTRIBUTION AND HABITAT: Brill can be found all round Britain and Ireland but are commonest in the south. They prefer sandy bottoms but are also found on gravel and mud. The younger smaller fish live in shallow water and tiny ones can be found in pools on the shore. Adults live mostly below 10m and down to about 70m. They can tolerate brackish water and so are also found in estuaries.

24

BIOLOGY: The fish spawn in spring and summer, mostly in shallow water between about 10–20m. The eggs and larval fish float in the plankton until the fish are between 20–35mm long. By this time they have changed into the adult flatfish shape and settle on the bottom, lying on their right sides. The young fish tend to stay in shallow water for a year or two. Brill mostly eat other fish, especially sand eels, whiting and gobies. They also eat large crustaceans such as crabs, and they take large numbers of squid. They are fished commercially, but are not as important or as good to eat as their relative the turbot.

BEHAVIOUR: Brill are well camouflaged when lying still on the bottom. Their large size may make them easier to spot than most of the smaller flatfish.

SIMILAR SPECIES: The most likely confusion is with the similar turbot but the brill has no bony tubercles on its back and the turbot has no frilly edge to the front of the dorsal fin. The other group of left-eyed flatfish are the topknots, mostly found in rocky areas.

KEY IDENTIFICATION FEATURES:

1. Wide body.

2. Frilly edge to front of
   dorsal fin.

3. Spotty appearance.

4. Curved lateral line.

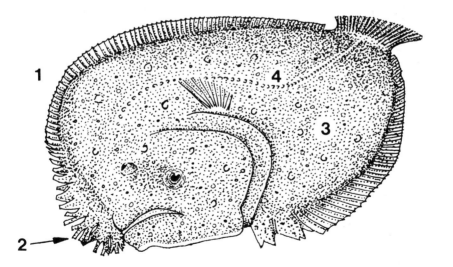

TURBOT *Scophthalmus maximus*

DESCRIPTION: The turbot is one of the largest flatfish, with a very broad body and wide fins. It appears rather like a large round dinner plate with a tail. The eyes are on the left side of the body. The front of the dorsal fin does not have the untidy frill-like appearance that is seen in the similar brill. The skin has no scales but instead there are large bony tubercles scattered over the body. However, these may be difficult to see through the spotted patterning. The lateral line is strongly arched over the pectoral fin. The colour is very variable as the fish can change it to suit the background. It is basically brown to greyish, with many irregular brown, blackish or greenish spots and lighter speckles which extend onto the tail and other fins. The underside is white, sometimes with darker blotches.

SIZE: The largest fish can reach 1m in length but 50–80cm (arms length) is more usual.

DISTRIBUTION AND HABITAT: Turbot can be found all round Britain and Ireland, but are commonest in the south. The preferred habitat is sand, gravel or shell-gravel, but it can also live in muddy areas and amongst mixed sand and rock. Adult fish live mostly below 20m down to about 80m, but smaller fish can be found right up to the shoreline. Recently settled fish less than a year old are common on sandy shores, especially in pools. It can also live in the brackish water of estuaries.

BIOLOGY: Like the brill, the turbot spawns in spring and summer in fairly shallow water, mostly between about 10–40m. Each female produces enormous numbers of eggs – in the region of 10–15 million. The eggs and larval fish float in the plankton and the young fish do not settle down onto the bottom until they are 4–6 months old and about 2.5cm long. Being left-eyed flatfish, they settle down in their right sides. During their floating existence they may be dispersed over a wide area, but eventually drift into and settle in shallow water. Turbot feed mostly on other fish, which they can easily catch with their large mouths. The prey are mostly sand-eels, sprats, herring, whiting and other cod fish; but gobies, flatfish dragonets, crustaceans and molluscs are also eaten. It is a very important and valuable commercial fish most of the catch coming from the central North Sea. It is caught in trawls, seine nets and on lines. Currently extensive efforts to cultivate turbot in captivity are proving promising.

BEHAVIOUR: Although the turbot is well camouflaged when lying on the seabed, it is a large thick fish, and the observant diver will soon learn to recognise which sand humps are alive. Local divers will often know of offshore banks where turbot can regularly be seen.

SIMILAR SPECIES: The round shape of the turbot should distinguish it from most other flatfish species. It could be confused with the brill (see comments on previous page).

KEY IDENTIFICATION FEATURES:

1. Large, almost round body.

2. Spotted or speckled appearance.

3. Scattered bony tubercles.

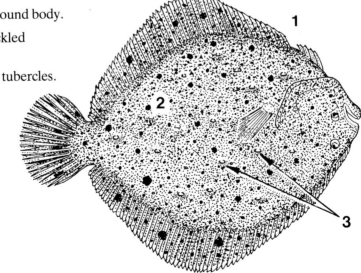

PLAICE   *Pleuronectes platessa*

DESCRIPTION: The plaice is a typical flatfish, and one that is often
seen by divers. It is oval in shape and is right-eyed (that is if the fish is
visualised swimming upright, then both the eyes are on the right side of the
body). Running between the eyes to the gill opening is a row of four to
seven bony knobs. The easiest way for the diver to recognise this fish is
from the colouration. The upper side is basically brown with numerous
conspicuous orange or red spots. Some individuals may also have smaller
white spots, especially when living in areas where the sediment has bits of
white shell or pebble. The lower side is white. They can change their
colour to suit the bottom, but the orange spots often give them away,
except when they are buried.

SIZE: The usual size limit is about 50–60cm (arm's length), but
exceptional specimens can reach nearly a metre in length (90cm).

DISTRIBUTION AND HABITAT: Plaice are common all round
Britain and Ireland, living mostly on sandy bottoms. They also live on
gravel and mud, and divers will frequently see them on sandy patches in
rocky areas. They are most common between 10–50m, but occur from
0–200m. Young fish in their first year live mostly in very shallow water and
can often be found in sandy tidal pools. They start to move into deeper
water in their second year when about 15cm long.

28

BIOLOGY: Plaice mostly spawn between January to March, each female producing up to half a million eggs. Around Britain, the eggs are laid in fairly shallow water between 20–40m in well-defined, spawning grounds. The largest of these areas lies midway between the Thames estuary and the Flemish Bight, and it is here that most plaice from the southern North Sea spawn. Adults may make long migrations to the spawning grounds. The eggs float near the surface and hatch after 2–3 weeks depending on the temperature. The larval fish are the normal upright symmetrical fish shape, and it is only after 4–6 weeks that they change into the flatfish shape and settle on the bottom. The most dramatic change is the migration of the left eye over to the right side of the body so that both eyes are on the same side. The young fish start to swim with their left blind side facing the seabed and eventually settle down when they are 10–17mm long, having drifted into the inshore nursery grounds. Plaice feed on bottom-living animals, particularly shellfish such as cockles and razor shells. These are crushed with the strong pharangeal teeth. They are also experts at nipping off the protruding siphons of deeply-buried clams. Worms, crustaceans, brittle stars and sand eels are also eaten. There is some evidence that young fish do not feed in winter but remain buried in the sand in a quiescent state. Plaice are one of Britain's most important commercial fish, and are caught in trawls and seine nets and by anglers. Fishery regulations are helping to conserve stocks, but plaice are slow-growing, living up to 30 years. Females only mature after 3–7 years and males after 2–6 years. Very large fish are now rarely caught.

BEHAVIOUR: Plaice spend much of their time lying quietly on the bottom, often partly buried. They will allow divers to approach closely and even touch them before swimming off. They are most active at night, and trawlers often make their best catches at this time.

SIMILAR SPECIES: The orange spots should distinguish the plaice from other flatfish.

KEY IDENTIFICATION FEATURES:

1. Bright orange or red spots.

2. Row of bony knobs on
   head.

3. Right-eyed.

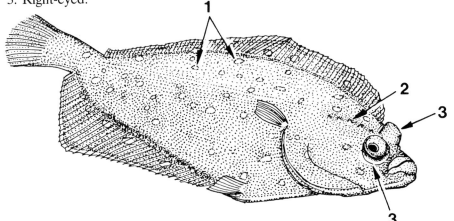

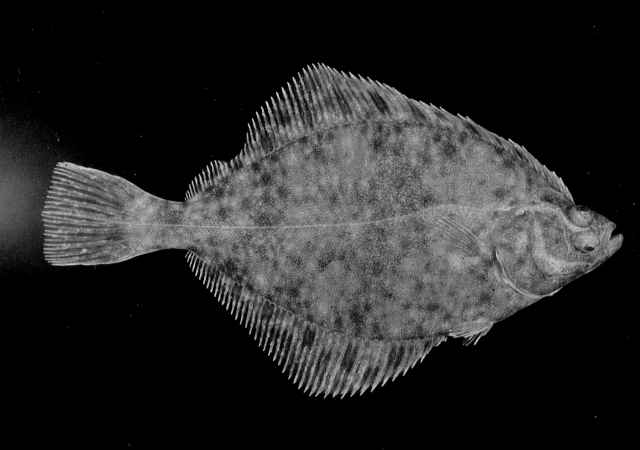

FLOUNDER $\qquad$ *Platichthys flesus*

DESCRIPTION: The flounder is another right-eyed flatfish (see description of plaice), oval in shape but slimmer than the plaice and with a dull brown or greeny-brown colouration that it can alter to match the background. Some fish have dull, indistinct reddish blotches, but these are nothing like the bright spots of the plaice. It is white on the underside. Along the bases of the dorsal and anal fins and irregularly along the lateral line, are rows of small bony tubercles, but these may be difficult to see underwater. The tail fin in the flounder is often rather square-cut, whilst in most other flatfish, it is rounded. Identification of the flounder is made more difficult by the fact that "reversed" individuals in which the eyes are on the left side of the body, are not uncommon. Also flounder occasionally interbreed with plaice, producing a hybrid with characteristics intermediate between the two species.

SIZE: The maximum length is about 50cm but few individuals over 30cm (forearm length) are seen or caught.

30

DISTRIBUTION AND HABITAT: The flounder is widely distributed, and is found all round Britain and Ireland. It lives on sandy and particularly on muddy bottoms from the shore down to at least 50m. The young in their first year tend to live in the very shallow water close inshore. The flounder is very tolerant to variations in salinity, and is frequently found in lagoons and estuaries penetrating right up into the fresh water of the rivers themselves. However, in the cold of the winter it is more likely to be found in the deeper, warmer water of the sea. It is not often seen by divers because of its preference for muddy areas.

BIOLOGY: In spring the adults move into deeper water of about 25–40m (around Britain) where they spawn. The females lay huge numbers of eggs, between half to two million, and these float near the surface. If the temperature is high enough (10°C) the eggs hatch after only about a week. The larval fish float in the plankton, but gradually sink as they grow and change into the adult form. This metamorphosis follows a similar pattern to that of the plaice, with one eye migrating over to join the other one and the fish lying down on its left side. This happens when they are about 1.5–3cm long, when they can be found on the bottom close inshore. The rate of growth varies, but they become sexually mature by 3 (males) to 4 (females) years old. Flounders feed on a variety of bottom-living animals – mainly shrimps, worms and a few molluscs such as cockles. However, they do not have the same ability as the plaice to crush up tough shellfish. The young fish eat small crustaceans such as sand hoppers and shrimps. Flounders are fished commercially, but are nowhere near as valuable as plaice.

BEHAVIOUR: Flounders spend most of the day buried in the sand, and so are not easy to spot. They are much more likely to be spotted on a night dive, when they are actively feeding in shallow water. They will move onto the shore at high tide and retreat as the tide falls.

SIMILAR SPECIES: The flounder is similar in shape and size to both the plaice and the dab. The plaice can be distinguished by its bright orange spots and the dab by the strong curve in the lateral line above the pectoral fin.

KEY IDENTIFICATION FEATURES:

1. Rows of bony tubercles at the bases of the dorsal and anal fins.

2. Square-cut tail fin.

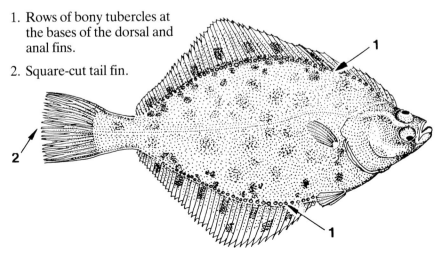

DAB   *Limanda limanda*

DESCRIPTION: The dab is a small and very common flatfish similar in general shape to the plaice and flounder. The eyes are on the right side of the body, and reversed individuals are relatively uncommon. The basic colour is brown with darker blotches and small speckles, but the pectoral fin is sometimes orange. Some fish may have a few orange spots, but these are not well developed as they are in the plaice. The most characteristic feature is the lateral line which can be quite clearly seen if the diver approaches the fish quietly. This is strongly arched into a semi-circular curve over the pectoral fin. If the fish can be touched, which is by no means impossible underwater, the skin on the upper surface will feel rough. Plaice and flounder feel smooth.

SIZE: Most dab reach only 25cm long (forearm length) but individuals up to 42cm have been found.

DISTRIBUTION AND HABITAT: Occurring all round Britain and Ireland, the dab is one of Britain's commonest flatfish and is particularly abundant in the North Sea. It lives in sandy areas from the shore down to

32

150m or so, but is commonest between 20–40m. The young live close inshore, usually in less than 1m of water, and the adults migrate inshore from deeper water in the warmer summer months.

BIOLOGY: The time of spawning depends on the water temperature, and therefore on latitude, but is in spring and early summer around Britain. Females produce up to 150,000 eggs which float near the surface and hatch after a week or two. The young fish settle down onto the seabed when they are about 1.5cm long, as they are completing their metamorphosis into the typical flatfish shape. Males can breed when they reach 2 years old and females when they are 3, and they can live for up to 12 years. Dab will eat almost any small bottom-living animal that they can catch. They will eat brittle stars, small sea urchins, fish, worms, crustaceans and molluscs. In spite of their small size they are a popular food fish, with a good flavour, and are moderately important commercially. They are caught in trawls and seine nets.

BEHAVIOUR: The dab has an interesting and characteristic method of feeding which it shares with the lemon sole. The fish raises its head and front part of the body up over a suitable site and waits for a worm or shellfish siphon to emerge. It then strikes rapidly down and bites it off. Like the flounder, it is most active at night.

SIMILAR SPECIES: The dab is similar in shape and colour to the flounder and lemon sole, but in these, the lateral line is straight or only slightly curved. See also key identification features for these species.

KEY IDENTIFICATION FEATURES:

1. Very distinct curve in lateral line.

2. No bony tubercles anywhere.

3. Rough skin on upper side.

4. Orange pectoral fin (not always).

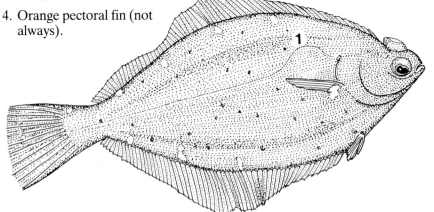

LEMON SOLE *Microstomus kitt*

LEMON SOLE *Microstomus kitt*

DESCRIPTION: The lemon sole should more accurately be called the lemon dab, since it is not a sole, and is shaped like a dab. It has a thicker body with more flesh than a dab. The eyes are on the right side of the body. The basic colour is brown but it usually has flecks of yellow and green as well as being mottled with darker brown or dull orange and yellow. Divers have also noticed that when it is found on rocks covered in pink encrusting algae (*Lithothamnion*) it often has distinct pink blotches. The underside is white. Unlike the dab's skin the lemon sole's is smooth and slimy to touch, and the lateral line has only a gentle curve.

SIZE: It does not usually grow to more than about 40cm (length of forearm including hand) but can reach nearly 70cm.

DISTRIBUTION AND HABITAT: The lemon sole is found all round Britain and Ireland, but is only locally common. It prefers slightly harder bottoms of firm sand or gravel, and also lives in stony and rocky areas. It ranges from a few metres depth down to about 400m, but only the small fish are found in shallow water.

34

BIOLOGY: Unlike the plaice, the dab does not have well-defined spawning grounds, but simply spawns in deep water of about 100m in spring and summer. The eggs and larval fish float in the plankton, and the young fish do not settle onto the bottom until they are about 3cm long. Males do not breed until they are about 3–4 years old and females until they are 4–6 years old. They can live for nearly 20 years. They feed mostly on soft-bodied animals such as worms and the siphons of bivalve molluscs, which they bite off with their sharp cutting teeth. The will also eat crustaceans and molluscs, including barnacles and chitons in rocky areas, but their small mouths and lack of powerful crushing teeth limit what they can take. In winter they rarely feed. It is a moderately important commercial fish and is caught in trawls.

BEHAVIOUR: Divers mostly encounter small lemon sole on rocks, where they remain quite still, relying on their camouflage to protect them. On sediment, a diver might be lucky enough to observe the method of feeding. The fish lifts its head and front part of the body up over a suitable worm hole or similar and waits until something emerges. It then strikes very quickly downwards before the prey can withdraw to safety.

SIMILAR SPECIES: The lemon sole is similar to but more colourful than the dab, which has rough skin and a curved lateral line. The only other flatfish likely to be encountered on rock are the topknots. These are all left-eyed flatfish.

KEY IDENTIFICATION FEATURES:

1. Often with colourful speckles.

2. Smooth slimy skin.

3. No bony tubercles anywhere.

4. Only slightly curved lateral line.

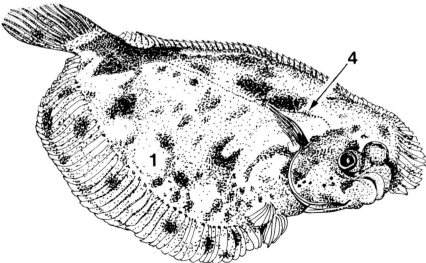

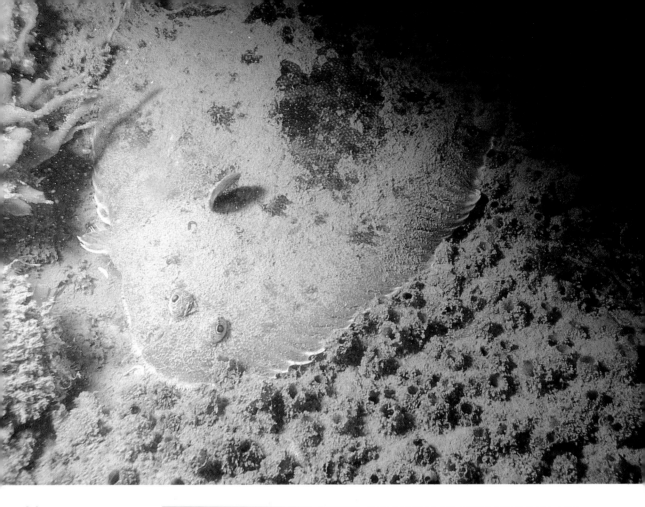

Sole.

SOLE or DOVER SOLE *Solea solea*

SOLENETTE *Buglossidium luteum*

DESCRIPTION: The sole is unlikely to be confused with any other flatfish, since the shape of its head is very characteristic. Below the rounded snout on the lower edge of the head is a small semi-circular mouth, which gives the fish a permanently sad expression. The eyes are on the right side of the body. The dorsal fin starts in front of the eyes, runs the whole length of the body and it, and the anal fin are joined to the tail fin. The anal fin is shorter, starting further back. The head has a fringe of short filaments around it. The sole is a master of camouflage, and can vary its colour to suit its background. The basic colour is brown with irregular darker blotches. The pectoral fin has a distinct black spot at its tip, and the edges of the dorsal and anal fins are usually whitish. The underside is white. The tiny solenette is very similar in shape to the sole. Apart from its small size, it can be distinguished by the very small pectoral fins (no black

36

spot) and the striped dorsal and anal fins in which every 5th or 6th ray is black. The general colour is a light sandy brown with darker spots.

SIZE: The usual maximum size for a sole is about 40cm (forearm with hand length) but they can reach 60cm. The tiny solenette reaches only 13cm (small hand size).

DISTRIBUTION AND HABITAT: Both species are widespread and common, occurring all round Britain and Ireland on sandy and muddy bottoms. The sole ranges from the shore, where very young fish live, down to 160m or so. The adults are more likely to be found in shallow water in summer since they migrate into deeper, warmer water in winter. The solenette lives between 5–40m, but is occasionally found much deeper. Occasionally divers see sole on boulders and amongst kelp, since they also frequent areas of mixed sand and rock.

BIOLOGY: The sole spawns in spring and summer in specific areas at depths of 40–60m. Each female produces up to 500,000 eggs which drift in the plankton. The larval fish hatch out after about 10 days (dependent on temperature), eventually becoming flatfish-shaped and settling on the bottom when about 12–15mm long. By this stage they have usually drifted into shallow water, and are often found in estuaries. Adults can breed when 3–5 years old. The solenette has a similar life history. Both species live on small bottom-living animals, especially small crustaceans and worms, but also molluscs and fish.

BEHAVIOUR: The sole spends the daytime buried in the sand with only the eyes showing. It is usually only seen by divers when they inadvertently disturb one or specifically search for them. Sole feed at night and are most active at dawn and dusk. If alarmed they will quickly bury themselves in the sand but leave the pectoral fin sticking out vertically. With its black tip, this fin resembles the poisonous dorsal fin of the weever fish and this may give the sole some protection.

SIMILAR SPECIES: Two other soles are found around Britain, the sand sole (*Pegusa lascaris*) and the thickback sole (*Microchirus variegatus*), but both are rare and generally found below 20–30m.

KEY IDENTIFICATION FEATURES:

1. Low-slung, semi-circular mouth.

2. Long dorsal and anal fins joined to tail.

3. Filaments around head.

4. Black mark on pectoral fin (sole).

5. Dorsal and anal fins striped with black (solenette).

ROKER or THORNBACK RAY
Raja clavata

DESCRIPTION: The roker is common in shallow water, and is the ray most often encountered by divers. Like all rays and skates it has a diamond-shaped body with the pectoral fins expanded to form "wings". The wing tips are rather pointed, forming a right angle, and the nose is short. As its alternative name suggests, the thornback is covered in sharp prickles. There are also numerous scattered large, backward pointing thorns (called bucklers) each of which has a thick button-like base. These thorns are particularly numerous on the tail and in females, in a line along the back. The thorns only develop fully as the fish become adult. The colour is very variable, usually a mottled, blotchy brown to grey, with numerous small dark spots and yellowish patches. In young fish the yellow patches form distinct spots, each outlined with smaller dark spots. The underneath is an off-white with grey to black margins.

SIZE: Rokers up to 1m long have been reported, but the usual maximum is 85cm. Females are larger than males.

DISTRIBUTION AND HABITAT: This ray is common all round Britain and Ireland on muddy, sandy and gravelly bottoms, and sometimes in areas of mixed sand and rock. It can be found from only a couple of metres deep down to at least 300m but is commonest between 10–60m.

BIOLOGY: Like all rays and skates, the roker mates, the male using a pair of rod-like claspers at the base of the tail to transfer sperm to the female. She does not bear live young as many sharks do, but instead lays her eggs enclosed in a "mermaid's purse" – an oblong, dark capsule 6–9cm long with a long horn at each corner (purses with tendrils belong to dogfish). The females come inshore to lay their eggs in spring, followed a little later by the males. The egg capsules are deposited from March to August, each female laying about 20 in all. The developing embryo takes 4–5 months to hatch, and is about 8cm across when it emerges. Whilst in the capsule, it receives fresh water through slits in the capsule horns and walls. In the summer, large numbers of young can be seen close inshore, and many empty mermaids' purses are washed ashore. Maturity is reached fairly late, with males breeding when about 7 years old and females when about 9 years. Roker feed on the bottom, mainly on crustaceans such as crabs and shrimps, but they will also take fish, molluscs, worms and echinoderms. The roker is caught in bottom trawls and is widely sold as "skate", along with the true skate, *Raja batis*.

BEHAVIOUR: Roker are often difficult to spot during the daytime, as they lie on the bottom covered in sand, with only the eyes and breathing holes (spiracles) showing. They emerge to feed at night. They can often be persuaded to swim off a little way, and will then settle back down on the surface, thus allowing clearer photographs to be taken. If touched, in the water or out, care should be taken of the sharp spines.

SIMILAR SPECIES: Other rays and skates have prickles and spines especially along the tail and midline but the large broad-based spines of the roker are characteristic.

KEY IDENTIFICATION FEATURES:

1. Prickly back.

2. Scattered large spines with broad bases.

3. Yellow eye spots on back especially in young fish.

CUCKOO RAY   *Raja naevus*

DESCRIPTION: The cuckoo ray is one of the prettiest European rays, and can be easily identified from its colouration alone. In the middle of each wing is a large and conspicuous black and yellow marbled spot, which shows up well against the basic grey-brown colour of the back. The underside is whitish or greyish, with darker patches. The wings of the cuckoo ray have rounded tips and the snout is short. There are 4–5 rows of closely-packed spines along the tail, and two rows along the mid-line of the body. Other patches of spines may also be present, and the skin of the back is prickly all over.

40

SIZE: The maximum size is just over half a metre long (70cm).

DISTRIBUTION AND HABITAT: The cuckoo ray can be found all round Britain and Ireland, but is most common in the south. It lives on sediment in depths of 20–150m. It is not often seen by divers, since it is most abundant at the deeper end of its range.

BIOLOGY: Few details have yet been recorded about the biology of this ray, but part of its life history is known. Females lay their egg capsules (mermaids' purses) all the year round, and each fish can produce up to 90 capsules during this time. The capsules are small, measuring about 6cm long and 3.5cm wide. They are a transparent brown, and have one long straight pair of horns and one shorter pair with incurved tips. The incubation period in the wild is not known, but in the aquarium is just over 8 months, with the young fish reaching about 12cm before hatching. The food of the cuckoo ray consists mainly of fish, plus worms, crustaceans and probably other bottom-living animals as well. This ray is of some commercial importance.

BEHAVIOUR: No readily available information. It is interesting to speculate whether the "eye" spots on the wings act as a deterrent to would-be predators.

SIMILAR SPECIES: No other European ray has similar markings.

KEY IDENTIFICATION FEATURES:

1. Large black and yellow eye-spot on each wing.

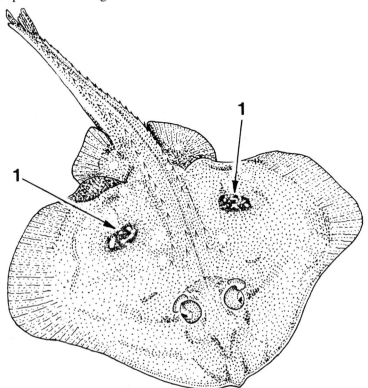

ANGLER FISH, FROG FISH or FISHING FROG *Lophius piscatorius*

DESCRIPTION: Like the rays and skates, the angler fish is flattened from top to bottom and spends most of its time lying on the seabed. However, its bizarre body form is unmistakable, and it cannot easily be confused with other bottom-living species. It is well camouflaged, and not always easy to spot. The head is broad and flattened, with a very large semi-circular mouth and long curved teeth, whilst the tail is short, thick-set and more normally fish-shaped. The angler fish gets its name from the characteristic fishing lure at the tip of a long filament just above the mouth. This is a modified dorsal fin ray. There are also a number of other shorter individual rays running along the back. All round the edge of the head and body are fringed lobes of skin, which break up the outline and help to camouflage the fish. The colour is very variable and may be brownish, reddish brown or greenish brown with darker blotches. The underneath (not normally seen by the diver) is very white, with black edges to the pelvic fins and darker edges to the pectoral and anal fins.

SIZE: Adults can reach a length of 2m but most are less than about 1.2m and divers will often come across much smaller individuals.

DISTRIBUTION AND HABITAT: The angler fish is common all round the coasts of Britain and Ireland, and can be found in water as shallow as 2m. However, it normally lives below about 18m on sandy, shelly, gravelly and sometimes muddy bottoms, often lying half buried. It is less often found amongst rocks, usually on sandy patches or on partly-buried rocks, and this is where most divers will see them.

BIOLOGY: Angler fish eggs are laid in a single layer in large ribbon-like gelatinous sheets as much as 9m long and 3m wide which float in the water column. However, they are rarely seen, since spawning occurs over very deep water, offshore, in spring and early summer. The young fish swim freely in the water column for a while and are helped to float by their very long fin rays. As the fish grows, the fins become relatively shorter, and at a length of about 8cm long the young fish take to a life on the seabed. One of the most interesting aspects of the angler fish's life is the way in which it feeds, and this can be seen by a patient and quiet diver. The angler preys mostly on smaller fish, which it attracts by gentle movements of the fishing lure. When they are within reach of the cavernous mouth they are rapidly engulfed. The teeth are depressible and directed backwards, so that there can be no escape for the prey. Flatfish, gobies, haddock, dogfish and many other fish species that live close to the seabed are all eaten, and so are many other bottom-living animals. There are also records of anglers leaving the bottom and dragging down sea birds from the surface. There is no commercial fishery for angler fish, but when they are caught, the tails are often marketed as "monkfish". The taste resembles that of prawns or other crustaceans.

BEHAVIOUR: The angler fish is so well camouflaged that it will often allow divers to approach very close and take photographs head-on, but beware of large specimens. An early biologist called Day, writing in 1888, suggests that angler fish can creep along the bottom using their pectoral fins and can therefore move without disturbing the water much and frightening off potential prey. Diver observations of this would be very interesting.

SIMILAR SPECIES: The diver is unlikely to encounter any other species of angler fish in British waters. The very similar black-bellied angler (*L. budegassa*) normally lives below 100m, and is very rarely found in shallow water.

KEY IDENTIFICATION FEATURES:

1. Large flattened head.

2. Large semi-circular mouth.

3. Fishing lure behind upper lip.

4. Frill of skin flaps.

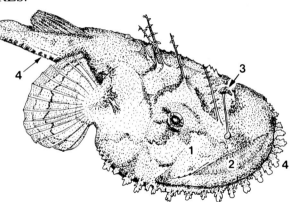

Common dogfish (left) and nursehound.

COMMON DOGFISH, LESSER SPOTTED DOGFISH, SANDY DOG or ROUGH HOUND
Scyliorhinus canicula

NURSEHOUND, GREATER or LARGER SPOTTED DOGFISH or BULL HUSS
Scyliorhinus stellaris

DESCRIPTION: Dogfish are small sharks with blunt heads and long, tapering bodies. Two small, rounded dorsal fins are set well back towards the tail. In common with all sharks, the mouth is on the underside and there are a number of gill slits along each side of the head. The common dogfish and the nursehound are very similar in overall appearance. Both are a sandy or greyish brown with dark brown spots or blotches and a creamy-white underside. Usually the two species can be distinguished by the size of the spots. The common dogfish has numerous small spots, whereas the nursehound has fewer and much larger spots, but unfortunately colour is not an infallible guide. The nursehound can sometimes have numerous spots or even be totally black. It is the common dogfish that is most frequently seen by divers. Other distinguishing features are of little use to the diver because they involve close examination of the fish (for instance on the underside of the head, all dogfish have grooves leading from the nostrils, and in the common dogfish these are connected to the mouth, whereas in the nursehound they are not).

SIZE: The common dogfish is the smaller of the two species, reaching 1m in length, but usually only 60 to 70cm. The nursehound on average is greater than 1m, and can reach 152cm.

44

DISTRIBUTION AND HABITAT: The common dogfish is very widely distributed all round Britain and Ireland, and sufficient numbers occur to support a small fishery. Dogfish are bottom-living sharks, and the common dogfish is mostly found on sandy, gravelly or sometimes muddy seabeds and in areas of mixed sand and rock. However, individuals are frequently seen by divers in shallow rocky areas where they come to lay their eggs. The nursehound in contrast lives mostly on rough or rocky grounds, and is much less abundant, only being really common in the south. Both species occur in very similar depth ranges from as shallow as 1m to well over 50m.

BIOLOGY: Dogfish lay their eggs individually in tough, leathery, pale brown cases commonly known as "mermaids' purses". These are firmly attached to seaweeds by long curling tendrils at each of the 4 corners. They are laid in shallow water and are a common sight in kelp forests and right up to low water mark. The young do not hatch until 5 to 11 months after the eggs were laid, and so are quite large on hatching – about 10cm for the common dogfish and 16cm for the nursehound. Since the eggs are laid already enclosed in their protective capsules, fertilization has to occur before the eggs are laid, and so dogfish mate in pairs. Mating occurs mainly in autumn, and the male coils himself around the female, and uses a pair of specially modified pelvic fins or claspers to help pass sperm into the female's genital opening. Egg capsules are laid some weeks later, mostly between November to July in the common dogfish, and spring and summer in the nursehound, although breeding can occur at any time. Dogfish are unfussy feeders, and will eat any small animals they can find on the seabed, such as crabs, shrimps, worms, whelks, sand eels and gobies.

BEHAVIOUR: Dogfish are mainly nocturnal, and during the day can frequently be seen lying "asleep" on the seabed. Divers can often pick them up in this state but they can easily coil their flexible bodies round and may try to bite!

SIMILAR SPECIES: Only one other dogfish, the blackmouthed dogfish (*Galeus melastomus*) occurs in British waters, but this is rarely found above about 55m depth.

KEY IDENTIFICATION FEATURES

1. Blunt head.

2. Two small rounded dorsal fins set far back.

3. Many small spots (common dogfish).

4. Fewer larger spots (nursehound).

Starry smooth hound.

STARRY SMOOTH HOUND
Mustelus asterias

SMOOTH HOUND
Mustelus mustelus

DESCRIPTION: Until recently, the starry smooth hound, which is quite common, was thought to be the immature stage of the much less common smooth hound. It is now certain that they are two distinct species. Both are small, slender sharks, with pointed snouts and two fairly large, almost equal-sized dorsal fins. Unlike the spurdog, smooth hounds do have an anal fin, so that on or near the underside there are two pairs of fins – the pectorals and pelvics – and a single anal fin. The colour is a plain grey above and a creamy white below, but as its name suggests, the starry smooth hound has numerous star-like white spots scattered over the back and sides.

SIZE: The usual size for both species is about 1m long, but the smooth hound can reach a maximum of 1.6m, and the starry smooth hound 1.8m.

DISTRIBUTION AND HABITAT: Both species occur all round Britain and Ireland, except that the smooth hound has not been recorded from the north of Scotland. They live close to the bottom, preferring a sand, mud or gravel substratum, from only a few metres depth down to about 100m.

BIOLOGY: Smooth hounds mate and bear live young, but the way the embryos develop is different in the two species. The starry smooth hound is ovoviviparous, the eggs hatching inside the mother's oviducts, but depending for nourishment on their own egg yolks. Seven to fifteen young are born in summer in shallow water after a gestation period of about a year, each one being about 30cm long. The smooth hound is viviparous,

46

and the eggs not only hatch inside the mother, but when the egg yolk is finished, the young are nourished through a connection of their yolk sacs to the mother. The litter size and newborn length are similar to those of the starry smooth hound. Smooth hounds feed mainly at night on a variety of crustaceans such as crabs, lobsters, hermit crabs and squat lobsters. A few other bottom-living animals, such as molluscs and fish, may also be eaten. Because the two species have only recently been distinguished, much previously recorded data on their biology could apply to either species.

SIMILAR SPECIES: The starry smooth hound is similar to the spurdog, particularly as they both have white spots. However, the spurdog has no anal fin and has a spine in front of each dorsal fin. The smooth hound is very similar to the tope. However, the smooth hound has equal-sized dorsal fins, whilst the tope has a much smaller second dorsal fin.

KEY IDENTIFICATION FEATURES:

1. Two large equal sized dorsal fins.

2. Anal fin present.

3. White spots on back and sides (starry smooth hound).

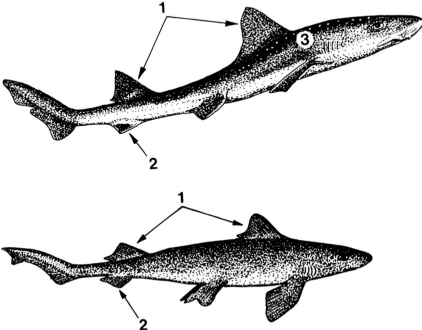

Juvenile spurdog.

SPURDOG or COMMON
SPINY DOGFISH   *Squalus acanthias*

DESCRIPTION: This small, slender shark has a pointed snout and large oval eyes. It is easy to distinguish from other small sharks because it has a sharp spine in front of each of the two widely-spaced dorsal fins. It also has no anal fin, so that on or near the underside, only two pairs of fins, the pectorals and pelvics, can be seen. The colour is a dark grey above, sometimes light grey or brownish, grading to white beneath. There are irregular white spots over the back and sides, but these are not always clear in old fish.

SIZE: The usual size is about a metre long with a maximum of about 1.2m. Females grow larger than the males.

DISTRIBUTION AND HABITAT: The spurdog is widespread and common, occurring all round Britain and Ireland. In summer they are particularly common around the Shetland Islands. They live near the seabed, over sand and mud, from about 10–200m, although they have been caught as deep as 950m. They are sometimes found in surface waters, especially at night.

48

BIOLOGY: Like many other sharks, the spurdog bears live young, the eggs hatching inside the mother's oviducts (ovoviviparous). The gestation period is very long, from 18–22 months, and between 3–11 young, each 20–30cm long are produced. The size and number of young depends on the size of the mother. Growth is slow, and the maximum life span has been calculated as 20–24 years. Spurdogs live on bottom-living animals such as crabs, flatfish, dragonets and cod, but also attack schools of herring, sprat, pilchards and other similar fish. Their habit of attacking netted fish earned them a reputation as pests that damaged fishing gear. However, a valuable fishery for them has recently developed, and they are eaten fresh or smoked, and are sold as "flake". Their slow growth and low reproductive capability means that they are likely to be over-exploited unless controls are implemented.

BEHAVIOUR: Spurdog usually occur in shoals, and in suitable areas these may number thousands of fish. However, most divers see only small shoals inshore. They migrate long distances, and often move many miles in a single day.

SIMILAR SPECIES: The tope (*Galeorhinus galeus*) and the smooth hounds (*Mustelus* spp.) are a similar colour, size and shape, but have no dorsal fin spines and do have an anal fin.

KEY IDENTIFICATION FEATURES:

1. Sharp spine in front of both
   dorsal fins.

2. No anal fin.

3. White spots on back and
   sides.

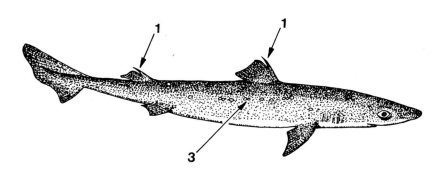

TOPE   *Galeorhinus galeus*

DESCRIPTION: The tope is a slender shark with a sharply-pointed snout and large pectoral fins. It has two dorsal fins, the first large but the second much smaller, and similar in size to the anal fin. This helps to distinguish it from the similar smooth hound, in which the dorsal fins are equal in size. The teeth are sharp and with the triangular shape typical of predatory sharks, and they are very different from the flat blunt teeth of the smooth hound. However, this may be difficult to see underwater. The colour is grey-brown on the back and sides, and whitish on the belly.

SIZE: The usual size is about 1.2m long, but adults can reach nearly 2m.

DISTRIBUTION AND HABITAT: Tope can be found all round Great Britain and Ireland. They live close to the bottom, preferring sand or gravel, but can also be found near the surface or in mid-water when feeding. Young fish live in shallow water near the shore, and the adults extend down to several hundred metres.

50

BIOLOGY: The tope has a similar life history to the spurdog and the smooth hound, and bears live young. Development is ovoviviparous – that is the eggs hatch inside the mother's oviduct but depend for their nourishment on their own egg yolk. The gestation period is about 10 months, and the females move inshore to give birth in late summer. Twenty to forty young are born, each about 40cm long. Tope feed mainly on fish, attacking schools of cod, bib and whiting, but they also feed on bottom-living animals such as crustaceans, flatfish and molluscs. Tope are not harvested commercially, but their fins are used in shark's fin soup, and small fish are considered edible. It is also a popular game fish.

BEHAVIOUR: Divers are most likely to see tope inshore in summer. They often live in small groups, but as they get older and larger, they tend towards a solitary existence.

SIMILAR SPECIES: The tope closely resembles the smooth hound in shape and colour. However, in the smooth hound the two dorsal fins are equal in size. The spurdog is also similar but has no anal fin and generally has white spots.

KEY IDENTIFICATION FEATURES:

1. Large first dorsal fin; small
    second dorsal fin.

2. Anal fin present.

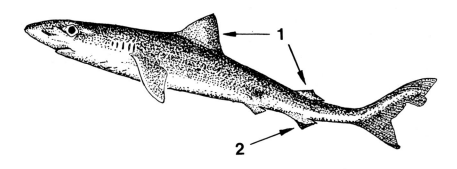

Tub gurnard (left) and red gurnard.

TUB GURNARD or
SAPHIRINE GURNARD   *Trigla lucerna*
RED GURNARD   *Aspitrigla cuculus*

DESCRIPTION: Gurnards are distinctive bottom-living fish, with large heads protected by hard bony plates with various spines. There are two dorsal fins and a single anal fin. The large pectoral fins have the first three rays as separate, thick, finger-like feelers. These are bent forward and used by the fish to feel for food in the sediment (see behaviour). The red gurnard has a row of large plate-like scales along the lateral line, which are not present in the tub gurnard. In overall colour, the two species can be very similar but the tub gurnard has distinctively-marked pectoral fins. The red gurnard is basically red with a pale underside. The tub gurnard is often red or pink all over, but can also be reddish-yellow, yellowish or brown, and may have brown or green blotches. The pectoral fins are always brilliantly marked with peacock blue. They may be almost totally blue, or have blue edges and blue or greenish spots with a dark blotch along the rear edge.

SIZE: The tub gurnard is the largest European gurnard, and can reach 75cm long. However, most are between 25–50cm (forearm to arm length without hand). The red gurnard reaches only 30–40cm (forearm and hand length).

DISTRIBUTION AND HABITAT: The tub gurnard occurs all round the coasts of Britain and Ireland. The red gurnard occurs on most coasts but is not found over most of the east coast of Britain. Both species live on sandy and muddy bottoms, but may be found in areas of mixed sand and rock. The tub gurnard is the commonest of the two, the red gurnard being

52

only locally common mostly on Atlantic coasts. Both can occur as shallow as 5m, but it is mostly the young that are found close inshore. Young of the red gurnard are often found in estuaries. The maximum depth limit is about 200–250m.

BIOLOGY: The spawning season is in spring and early summer, and the eggs and larval fish float freely in the plankton. Gurnards feed mainly on crustaceans such as crabs and shrimps but the tub gurnard in particular also eats bottom-living fish such as gobies, sand eels, young flatfish and dragonets. It is a good swimmer, and can also catch sprats, pilchards and sand smelts. The tub gurnard is caught in trawls, and is a moderately important commercial fish. The red gurnard is also caught, but in lesser numbers.

BEHAVIOUR: Gurnards can often be quite closely approached by divers, and with their brilliant colours, make good photographic subjects. They use their three pectoral feelers both to walk along the bottom and to probe for food, since the feelers have sensitive taste buds. Sometimes they will sit propped up on their feelers or will rest flat on the bottom. If frightened they can swim very fast, and the tub gurnard will even jump above the water surface. They tend to be found in small schools, and can sometimes be heard making short, sharp, grunting noises, which may help to keep the school together. The noise comes from vibrations of the swim bladder walls by special muscles.

SIMILAR SPECIES: Unlikely to be confused with other groups of fish. Red mullet have two long barbels on the chin with which they search for food, but these only superficially resemble the gurnard's pectoral feelers.

KEY IDENTIFICATION FEATURES:

1. Large bony head with steep profile.

2. Three distinctive pectoral fin feelers.

3. Red colour (red); variable colour (tub).

4. Peacock blue markings on pectoral fins (tub).

GREY GURNARD *Eutrigla gurnardus*

DESCRIPTION: The grey gurnard is very similar in general appearance to the red and tub gurnards. It has all the typical gurnard features, with a large bony head, two dorsal fins and three finger-like pectoral feelers. The scales along the lateral line each have a sharp spine, most noticeable in small fish. As the name suggests, the basic colour is grey, varying from greyish-brown to greyish-red, with numerous small whitish or yellowish spots. The underneath is an off-white. There is a characteristic black or greyish blotch on the edge of the first dorsal fin.

SIZE: The usual adult size is around 30cm (forearm length) but it can reach 45cm.

DISTRIBUTION AND HABITAT: The grey gurnard is widely distributed and occurs all round Britain and Ireland. It is especially common on Atlantic coasts, preferring muddy and sandy bottoms. It can also live in areas of mixed sand and rock and on gravel. The preferred depth range is between 20–50m, but it is found as shallow as 10m and as deep as 200m. It is more often found inshore in summer.

BIOLOGY: It spawns in the summer between April and August, the female laying between 200,000 and 300,000 eggs which float in the plankton. These hatch after about 10 days, and the larval fish live and feed in the plankton before finally settling on the bottom. The maximum life span is about 6 years. The adults feed on bottom-living animals, mostly shrimps and crabs, but also small fish, in the same way as the tub and red gurnards. It is incidentally – caught in trawls, and although not as popular as the tub gurnard, it is marketed in small amounts.

BEHAVIOUR: The behaviour is very similar to that of the tub and red gurnards. It uses its pectoral feelers to walk about on the bottom and search for food, and it is able to make grunting noises.

SIMILAR SPECIES: The dark blotch on the first dorsal fin should distinguish it from other gurnard species. See also comments under tub gurnard.

KEY IDENTIFICATION FEATURES:

1. Large bony head with steep profile.

2. Three distinctive pectoral fin feelers.

3. Black/grey blotch on first dorsal fin.

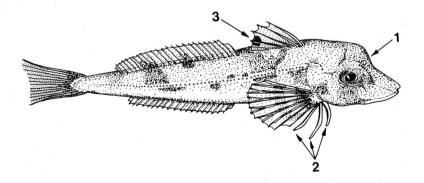

HOOKNOSE, POGGE or ARMED BULLHEAD *Agonus cataphractus*

DESCRIPTION: The hooknose is a very distinctive, easily recognised little fish. Viewed from above, it has a wide, triangular head and a tapering body, which has a long, thin, rear half. Instead of scales, it is completely covered in hard, bony, plates, giving it a rigid inflexible look. There is a strong spine on each gill cover, and a pair of curved spines on the snout from which the common name of hooknose is derived. Around the mouth and on the underside of the head are numerous short barbels which help it to find food. There are two short dorsal fins set close together, and one anal fin. It is dull brown in colour, with 4 or 5 darker saddles over the back, and it blends in well with the background. The belly is whitish and the pectoral fins have orange tints in the breeding season.

SIZE: An average hooknose would fit easily into the palm of the hand, the usual size being 10 to 15cm. Some occasionally reach 20cm or so.

56

DISTRIBUTION AND HABITAT: The hooknose is common all round Britain and Ireland, living mostly in sandy and muddy areas. The young can be found in as little as 2m of water, but adults mostly live below 20m down to several hundred metres. They are not often seen by divers, probably because they spend much of their time partly buried in the sediment, and diving in deep, muddy areas is not popular amongst divers.

BIOLOGY: Females spawn mostly between February and May, depositing clumps of yellow eggs amongst kelp (*Laminaria*) holdfasts and the holdfasts of other large brown seaweeds. Presumably those living in deep water make inshore migrations to spawn in the shallows. The eggs are not guarded by either parent, and may take as long as 12 months to hatch. The young larvae drift and disperse in the plankton, settling down on the bottom when they reach about 2cm long. The hooknose feeds on the bottom, searching out small crustacea with its snout and sensory barbels. It also eats brittlestars, worms and small molluscs.

BEHAVIOUR: Relying on its dull colours for camouflage, the hooknose will often remain quite still when approached. Its inflexible body makes it a poor swimmer, and it relies on its bony casing for protection from predators.

SIMILAR SPECIES: The hooknose is the only representative of its family found in British waters. It might at first glance be mistaken for a female dragonet, which is similar in shape, but the two are easily told apart.

KEY IDENTIFICATION FEATURES:

1. Two dorsal fins.

2. Armoured body.

3. Numerous small barbels
   under the head.

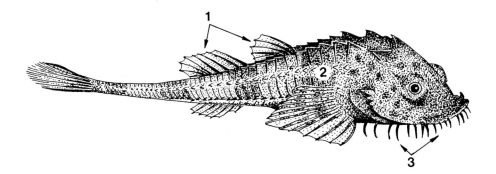

Male dragonet in mating colours (left) and female dragonet.

DRAGONET   *Callionymus lyra*

RETICULATED DRAGONET
Callionymus reticulatus

DESCRIPTION: Dragonets are bottom-living fish, with rather flattened bodies, and when viewed from above, the head appears almost triangular. The eyes are fairly large and set close together on top of the head. All the fins are large, particularly in the males. There are two dorsal fins, the first of which is triangular, and which in the males, (especially those of the common dragonet) have a very long first ray. However, these fins are normally kept folded back along the body of the fish, and may not be obvious. Most sightings of dragonets are of the drab, pale blotchy-brown females or immature males of the common dragonet. These have six greenish or brownish blotches along the sides, and three dark saddles across the back. The reticulated dragonet is not often seen by divers, since it is relatively uncommon. In the reticulated dragonet, the females and immature males are orange-brown, with four dark-edged red-brown saddles across the back, and a "spotty" appearance, due to numerous pale blue spots along the sides. Male common dragonets are relatively rarely seen by divers, but their spectacular colours make them easy to spot. They have numerous blue stripes and blotches all over the basically brown body, and all the fins are similarly striped. In the reticulated dragonet, the males are similar in colour to the females, but the dorsal fins have dark-edged spots and bluish-white wavy lines. The first dorsal fin ray is not so dramatically elongated as in the common species.

SIZE: The common dragonet is the larger of the two species, with females reaching 20cm (large hand length) and males 30cm. Females of the reticulated dragonet reach only about 8cm and males about 10cm (palm sized).

DISTRIBUTION AND HABITAT: The dragonet is widespread and abundant, occurring all round Great Britain and Ireland. It lives on sandy

58

and muddy bottoms, from a few metres depth down to at least 200m, although it is commonest above 100m. The reticulated dragonet is much more restricted, and is found only along the south and west coasts of Britain, around southern Ireland and in the Irish Sea. It lives on sand and shell bottoms from low water mark to about 40m.

BIOLOGY: The common dragonet spawns from late winter well into the summer, the month depending on the locality. The brightly-coloured males perform an elaborate display to attract the females, and this involves spreading out and erecting their beautiful fins. Each pair of fish then swims up vertically side by side towards the surface and spawns in mid-water. The fertilised eggs and young larvae that hatch from them float in the plankton until development is complete and the young fish can settle down on the bottom. The life span is about 5 years for males and 7 for females. Dragonets feed on a variety of small animals that they find buried in the sediment. Worms, shellfish and small crustaceans are the staple diet. The biology of the reticulated dragonet has been very little studied. It is thought to spawn in summer in the English Channel, since young fish are found in the plankton from May to September.

BEHAVIOUR: The female dragonet is well camouflaged, and will often partly bury itself in the sandy bottom. When disturbed by a diver, it will swim rapidly off just above the bottom, stopping again a few metres further on. Sometimes, puffs of muddy water are blown out from the gill openings which are situated high up on the sides of the body, and this is probably part of the feeding process.

SIMILAR SPECIES: A third species, the spotted dragonet (*C. maculatus*) occurs around Great Britain, and is very similar to the reticulated dragonet. However, it generally lives in deeper water – below about 70m on offshore sandy banks. Female dragonets are sometimes confused by divers with the bull-rout (*Myoxocephalus*) which has a similar body shape and can be found on sand.

KEY IDENTIFICATION FEATURES:

1. Flattened body; triangular head; eyes on top.

2. Two dorsal fins; first triangular.

3. Colourful males with long first ray in first dorsal fin.

4. Both sexes with pale blue spots on sides (reticulated dragonet).

RED MULLET   *Mullus surmuletus*

DESCRIPTION: The red mullet belongs to a family of fish (Mullidae) that live mostly in tropical areas, where they are known as goat fish. It is the only species that lives in British waters, and it is easily recognised from the characteristic pair of long barbels on the chin, which are constantly in motion as the fish swims over the seabed. It has a relatively slender body, a smooth, steep, profile to the head, two dorsal fins, and large, fragile scales. The colour varies with depth, time of day and emotional state of the fish. Those in shallow water above about 15m are basically a yellow or reddish brown, whilst those in deeper water are mostly red. During the day, and especially when the fish are in shoals, there is a dark red or brown line running through the eye to the tail and 4 or 5 other yellowish lengthwise stripes. At night the pattern breaks up, giving an indistinct marbled effect. When the fish are caught and are dying, they go through a rapid and beautiful series of colour changes.

SIZE: The maximum size is about 40cm – the length of a hand and forearm – but it is more usual to see shoals of smaller fish.

60

DISTRIBUTION AND HABITAT: Red mullet can be found all round Great Britain and Ireland, although they are not common. In the Channel and the southern North Sea they can at times be quite numerous, and it is probable that the numbers are swollen in the summer by fish migrating north from the Mediterranean and further south. It lives mostly in sandy and muddy areas, and its method of feeding is adapted to this habitat. However, young fish can be found browsing through algae-covered rocks as shallow as 1m. Adults range mostly from 3m down to about 90m.

BIOLOGY: It is not known exactly where and when red mullet breed in British waters, but in the Mediterranean they spawn in summer. The eggs are laid on the seabed between 10 to 55m. On hatching, the young fish drift in the plankton until they are about 5cm long. At this stage they are a silvery blue colour, which provides a good camouflage in the open water. The feeding behaviour is typical of all goat fish which use their long, sensitive, chin barbels to probe the sediment for small animals. When they find something edible they will dig energetically down to some depth in search of their prey. Around Britain, red mullet are too scarce to be commercially exploited, but they are a much-prized food fish, and fetch a good price when they are caught.

BEHAVIOUR: Red mullet can be recognised instantly from the way they swim slowly over the seabed flicking their chin barbels as they search for food. They often occur in shoals of up to 50 fish, but can also be found singly. When they are resting quietly on the bottom, they can be closely approached by a diver. However, they will eventually swim off, and the erection of the first dorsal fin by some fish seems to act as a signal to the rest. Shoals of mullet are often accompanied by other species, such as sea-bream and wrasse, which are on the look-out for food items stirred up by the mullet.

SIMILAR SPECIES: The pair of long, sensory, chin barbels should distinguish this fish from all others in British waters.

KEY IDENTIFICATION FEATURES:

1. Two dorsal fins.

2. Two long barbels under the chin.

3. Bottom living.

BLACK GOBY — *Gobius niger*

DESCRIPTION: The black goby is large and thick-set, and as its name suggests, is dark in colour. It varies from medium to dark brown, with darker blotches and reticulations, the exact colour depending on age and habitat. Like all gobies it has two dorsal fins and the most reliable identification feature is the first dorsal fin, which has elongated fin rays, giving it a pointed, almost triangular look. This is most obvious in males. Both dorsal fins have a dark spot on the top front edge, but this is not always very distinct. These characteristics are obviously easier to see when the fins are erect.

SIZE: One of the larger gobies, reaching a maximum of about 17cm; about hand sized.

62

DISTRIBUTION AND HABITAT: One of the most widely distributed gobies, occurring all round the coasts of Britain and Ireland. In contrast to the rather similar rock goby, it lives in muddy and sandy areas, and is particularly common in sea grass beds. It can tolerate low salinities, and so is also common in estuaries, coastal lagoons and sea lochs. In sheltered Scottish sea lochs, it can be found amongst the silt-covered rocks around the edges as well as on the sediment in deeper water. It has a depth range of from 2m or so down to about 70m.

BIOLOGY: The breeding follows a similar pattern to that of other gobies and blennies. The female lays her eggs inside old mollusc shells or under loose rocks, attaching them firmly by one end so that they form a dense patch. The male then guards them until they hatch. The black goby feeds mostly on small crustaceans such as shore crabs and small fish, molluscs and worms.

BEHAVIOUR: Some diver observations suggest that this goby may sometimes live in association with the Norway lobster (*Nephrops norvegicus*), hiding in its burrows. However, this has not been confirmed, and the sightings may have been of Fries's goby (*Lesuerigobius friesii*), a relatively rare, deep-water goby, known to have this association. A relatively large goby that could be the black goby has also been observed by amateur divers, living in the excavations made by lobsters in the sediment under rocks, but the species involved has not been identified.

SIMILAR SPECIES: Confusion may occur with the rock goby and possibly the painted goby. The rock goby is similar in size and colour, being almost black at times. However, it is confined to rocky areas, whereas the black goby prefers sand and mud. The black goby sometimes appears to have spots on the dorsal fins similar to those of the painted goby. However, the painted goby is much smaller, and has much clearer spots.

KEY IDENTIFICATION FEATURES:

1. Pointed first dorsal fin.

2. Black spots in front corners of both dorsal fins.

3. Lives on or near sediment.

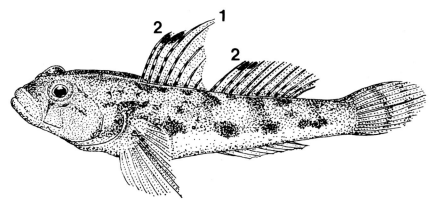

PAINTED GOBY   *Pomatoschistus pictus*

DESCRIPTION: The painted goby is one of three small gobies often seen by divers in sand and gravel areas (see under similar species below). All are a brownish or fawn colour, and at first glance appear very similar. However, they can be identified by careful observation of the habitat and behaviour as well as the colour. The painted goby is characterised by a series of distinct black spots arranged in rows across the bases of the two dorsal fins – very obvious when the fins are erect. There is also a line of four "double" black spots along the middle of both sides, but these are not so easily seen. The background colour is a warm, reticulated brown or fawn, with paler saddles reaching down the sides. However, males can be quite bright, especially in the breeding season, when the pink or orange banding often present on the dorsal fins above the black spots may be enhanced.

SIZE: Most adults are about thumb-sized i.e. about 6cm, but some grow to 9.5cm.

DISTRIBUTION AND HABITAT: This moderately common goby is found all round the coasts of Britain and Ireland, except for the east coast of England, where it has not been recorded. It lives on fairly coarse sediment bottoms of gravel, shell gravel, or sand mixed with shells and stones, and is often found sheltering inside empty bivalve shells. It is also found in sea grass and horse mussel beds, and occasionally in shore pools with stony bottoms. Unlike the common and sand gobies, it does not venture into estuaries. It ranges from low tide level to about 50m.

BIOLOGY: The painted goby lays its small, slightly elongated eggs inside empty bivalve mollusc shells so that they usually hang down from the roof of the hidey hole. This occurs between April and July, and like many other gobies, the male painted goby carefully guards the eggs until they hatch. The tiny larvae about 3mm long float in the plankton until they reach about 12mm, when they settle down to a life on the seabed. The need for suitable empty shells for egg laying partly determines the choice of habitat of this species. Little has been written about the diet of this goby, but it presumably feeds on small animals present in the sediment on which it lives.

BEHAVIOUR: This little goby appears remarkably unafraid of divers. Rather like the garden robin, painted gobies soon appear, looking for titbits, when a diver digs into the sediment, and if the diver backs off, will busily search around in any holes he has dug.

SIMILAR SPECIES: The sand goby (*P. minutus*) and the common goby (*P. microps*) are similar in size and background colour, but lack the rows of black spots on the dorsal fins.

KEY IDENTIFICATION FEATURES:

1. Both dorsal fins have rows
   of black spots.

2. Four small double dark
   spots along sides.

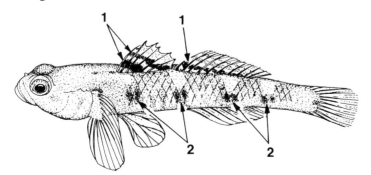

Sand goby.

COMMON GOBY *Pomatoschistus microps*
SAND GOBY *Pomatoschistus minutus*

DESCRIPTION: These two sand-coloured gobies are very difficult to tell apart under water, but with a little practice, can usually be distinguished from other species such as the painted goby. The colour of both species is a light grey to sandy brown, with darker reticulations and dots on the back. Both have a dark triangular mark at the tail base, and in the males there is a conspicuous black spot on the rear edge of the first dorsal fin. There are subtle differences but these are difficult to spot under water. The common goby usually has a triangular mark on the base of the pectoral fin, which the sand goby does not. Other differences can only be seen in captive fish, with the use of a hand lens. Slight differences in the habitat are also useful (see below).

SIZE: The common goby reaches 6.4cm and the sand goby is usually around 6cm (size of little finger), but can reach 9.5cm.

DISTRIBUTION AND HABITAT: Common and sand gobies are both abundant all round the coasts of Britain and Ireland. They live close inshore or onshore in sandy and muddy areas. The common goby tends to live higher up the shore, and is mostly found in high-shore pools on sandy beaches, or on muddy and marshy shores. However, it tends to move into deeper water in winter. It can tolerate low salinities, and this is the little goby so often seen in estuaries, salt marshes and brackish drainage ditches. The sand goby lives from about mid-tide level to 20m depth, and again moves into deeper water in winter. Unlike the common goby, it cannot tolerate low salinities, and only gets as far as the mouths of estuaries. Thus a diver in summer swimming over sandy or muddy areas is most likely to see the sand goby, but in winter might encounter either species.

BIOLOGY: The eggs of both species are laid inside old bivalve shells between March and August, and are guarded by the males. The male sand goby constructs quite an elaborate nest. After finding a suitable shell such as a cockle shell, he turns it concave side down and excavates a chamber underneath it with a tunnel entrance. He then covers the whole thing with loose sand before persuading his mate to lay her eggs inside. On hatching, the young larvae float in the plankton until they reach about 17mm long. Most live for only a year. Females of the common goby lay several broods of eggs, and by the end of the summer thousands of tiny gobies can be seen in sheltered shady pools. Both species feed mainly on crustaceans, including copepods, amphipods (sand hoppers) and young shrimps. The sand goby in turn is eaten by many bottom-living fish such as the bull-rout and pouting. The common goby probably forms an abundant food supply for fish and sea birds, but little work has been done on its predators.

BEHAVIOUR: There are few observations on the behaviour of these two species.

SIMILAR SPECIES: The two species themselves are difficult to tell apart. The only other small (less than 8cm) goby likely to be found on sediment is the painted goby, which can be identified from the rows of black spots along the dorsal fin bases.

KEY IDENTIFICATION FEATURES:

1. Small sand coloured gobies.

2. Triangular mark at the tail base (also in painted goby).

3. No obvious dorsal fin marks except black mark on rear edge of first dorsal fin (males).

4. Common goby has dark mark at top base of pectoral fin.

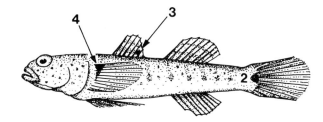

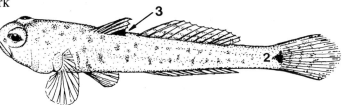

BUTTERFLY BLENNY *Blennius ocellaris*

DESCRIPTION: Resembling the tompot blenny in general shape, this large, stout blenny also has a bushy tentacle on the head above each eye. However, it can be recognised easily, provided the single, long dorsal fin can be seen. When erect, this fin is very high, with an extra-long first ray, and on the front half, a large black spot encircled by pale blue or white. The single dorsal fin is also deeply notched in the middle. There is a small fleshy flap at the base of the first dorsal fin ray and at the top edge of the pectoral fin, but these are small, and may not be obvious to a diver. The fish is a greenish-brown with 5 to 7 darker vertical bands running down the sides.

SIZE: Adults can grow to 20cm – about the length of a man's hand.

DISTRIBUTION AND HABITAT: The butterfly blenny has a southern distribution, and has only been recorded from south and west coasts of Britain, as far north as southern Scotland, and round most of Ireland except for the north coast. It is usually found on rough ground such as shell gravel, in maerl beds (calcareous seaweed) or where *Lithothamnion* (encrusting pink seaweed) is common. However, it also lives on sand, sheltering inside old mollusc shells, or anything else it can find such as discarded tin cans, crockery and other debris. It lives in relatively deep water from about 10m to 100m.

BIOLOGY: The female lays her eggs in spring and summer, sticking them to the inside of shells or other shelters or in rock crevices and, as in other blennies, the male guards the eggs until the larvae hatch and drift off in the plankton. After a few weeks the young fish settle down to live on the seabed. Few observations have been made on the diet of this blenny, but it eats whatever it can catch near to its shelter, such as small crustaceans, fish and worms.

BEHAVIOUR: Few specific observations have been recorded on the natural behaviour of this beautiful blenny.

SIMILAR SPECIES: Montagu's, Tompot and Yarrell's blennies all have large head tentacles and might be confused if only the head can be seen, but the spot on the dorsal fin will distinguish the butterfly blenny.

KEY IDENTIFICATION FEATURES:

1. High dorsal fin with a long first ray and a black spot encircled by pale blue or white.

2. A bushy tentacle above each eye.

3. Small fleshy flaps.

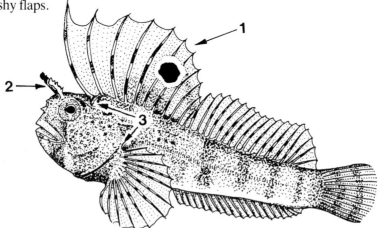

VIVIPAROUS BLENNY
or EELPOUT
Zoarces viviparous

DESCRIPTION: This slimy eel-like fish should more accurately be called the viviparous eelpout, since it is not a blenny at all. It is the only representative of the eelpout family (Zoarcidae) found around our shores. It has a long body with a large broad head and thick lips, giving it a blenny-like look. The dorsal, anal and tail fins are joined such that a single long fin runs right round the body. There is a distinct dip in the dorsal fin near the tail where the fin rays are very short. The pectoral fins are large and fan-like, whilst the pelvic fins are reduced to short stumps. The colour is variable – greyish-brown, yellowish-brown or dark brown on the back with a paler belly. There are darker bars on the back and blotches on the sides. The pectoral fins are edged with yellow or orange, but may be bright red in breeding males.

SIZE: The usual size is about 30cm (about forearm length), but it can grow to 50cm.

70

DISTRIBUTION AND HABITAT: The eelpout is basically a northern species, and is found off the northern tip of Ireland, all round Scotland, and down the east coast of Britain to the eastern end of the Channel. It lives on and sometimes burrows into muddy and sandy bottoms, including river estuaries, and extends from the shore down to 40m, but is most common in shallow water. On the shore it can be found in rocky areas in pools and under algae.

BIOLOGY: As its name suggests, the viviparous blenny gives birth to live young. The fish mate between August and September, but instead of being laid, the eggs develop and hatch after 3 to 4 weeks inside the female's single ovary. The young remain inside the female for about 4 months, and are then born between December and February at a length of about 4cm. The number of young produced depends on the size of the female, and varies from about 20 to 300 or so. The eelpout feeds on crustaceans, small fish, and any other small animals it can catch. In the Baltic it is commercially fished, but this is not the case around Great Britain.

BEHAVIOUR: There appear to be few observations on the behaviour of this fish.

SIMILAR SPECIES: The snake blenny (*Lumpenus lampretaeformis*) is similar in size and shape, but generally occurs in deeper water. Young fish might be confused with the butterfish (*Pholis gunnellus*), but this has very distinctive markings.

KEY IDENTIFICATION FEATURES:

1. Eel-like shape.

2. Continuous fin round the body.

3. Distinct dip in dorsal part of fin near tail.

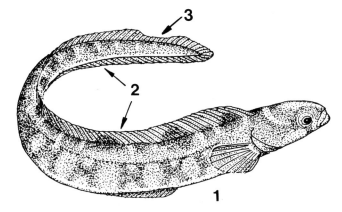

Greater pipefish.

GREATER PIPEFISH   *Syngnathus acus*

NILSSON'S PIPEFISH
Syngnathus rostellatus

DESCRIPTION: These two pipefish are difficult to tell apart underwater, but can usually be distinguished from other pipefish. As the name implies, pipefish have long thin tube-like bodies and elongated snouts. The body is encased in a tough armour of segmented plates which gives them a very stiff appearance. In the greater and Nilsson's pipefish, the arrangement of the plates gives the body an angular look and feel, and in cross-section the body is polygonal. Both these species have well-developed pectoral and tail fins – a useful distinguishing feature from some of the other pipefish. A close examination is necessary to tell the difference between these two species. The greater pipefish has a long snout more than half the total head length, and there is a conspicuous hump on the top of the head behind the eyes. In Nilsson's pipefish the snout is shorter than half the head length, and it has no hump behind the

72

eyes. Both species are a similar brownish to greenish colour with alternating light and dark bands, and both are lighter below.

SIZE: The greater pipefish can reach 47cm (forearm and hand length) and specimens up to 30cm are common. In contrast, Nilsson's pipefish reaches only 17cm (hand-sized). Thus large greater pipefish are easily distinguished.

DISTRIBUTION AND HABITAT: The two species are found all round Great Britain and Ireland in shallow coastal water over mud and sand bottoms and also in estuaries. A favourite habitat is amongst seagrass, seaweeds and floating algal debris. Nilsson's pipefish is the commoner of the two, living mostly above 10m, whereas the greater pipefish extends down to 20m.

BIOLOGY: The pipefish are an interesting group of fish in which the male carries and protects the eggs. In both the above species the male has a brood pouch under the tail formed by a fold of skin, and the female lays her eggs into the pouch where they are fertilized by the male. So individuals seen carrying eggs are males not females. The young hatch inside the pouch and finally leave home after a few weeks when they are about 20–30mm long (greater) or 14mm long (Nilsson's). Even after leaving the pouch, the young fish may at first return to it if danger threatens. Egg-carrying males are found mostly in the summer between June and August. Pipefish feed mostly on small, floating organisms such as copepods, and very young fish. These are carefully stalked and then sucked into the mouth by an expansion of the tubular snout.

BEHAVIOUR: Pipefish are often difficult to spot underwater since their camouflage is very good. They tend to lie along seaweed fronds at the same angle to them. Once spotted they can often be picked up, especially at night. They swim quite slowly, with a snake-like motion, bending the body from side to side, and they also use the dorsal fin.

SIMILAR SPECIES: The deep-snouted pipefish is similar to these two species, but has a distinctly broader and laterally-compressed snout.

KEY IDENTIFICATION FEATURES:

1. Long tubular body and head.

2. Dorsal, pectoral and tail fins present. No anal or pelvic fins.

3. Polygonal in cross section.

4. Long snout (greater) short snout (Nilsson's).

5. Hump on head behind eyes (greater only).

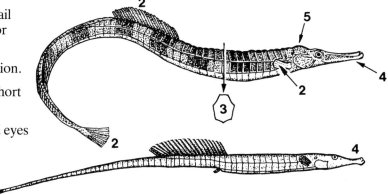

DEEP-SNOUTED or BROAD-SNOUTED PIPEFISH *Syngnathus typhle*

DESCRIPTION: This pipefish has a similar body shape to the greater and Nilsson's pipefish, and like them has well developed pectoral and tail fins. However, it is distinguished from them by the deep snout, which instead of narrowing in front of the eyes, is the same depth as the rest of the head. The snout is also flattened from side to side, not tubular as in the other two species. The whole of the head profile is thus smooth, with the top of the head and snout forming a more or less straight line. In colour it is a light greeny-brown or brown, paler below and sometimes with a few vertical bars.

SIZE: A large pipefish reaches about 30cm maximum size (about forearm length). Males reach maturity by about 12cm long.

DISTRIBUTION AND HABITAT: Found all round Great Britain and Ireland, this species lives in shallow coastal waters down to about 20m. It is fairly common, and can be locally abundant, particularly in seagrass beds in sandy areas. However, it can also be found in rocky areas amongst seaweeds. It can tolerate low salinities such as those found in estuaries and sea lochs.

BIOLOGY: The breeding biology of the deep-snouted pipefish follows the same pattern as the greater and Nilsson's pipefish. Breeding occurs in the summer, and egg-carrying males can be found from June to August. The young leave the brood pouch after about 4 weeks' incubation, and at a length of about 2.5cm. They are fully developed miniatures of their parents. The diet is also similar in this species, consisting mainly of copepods, other small crustaceans, and fish fry. It eats more of the latter than the other pipefish, perhaps because of its wider mouth and snout.

BEHAVIOUR: When amongst seagrass and long-fronded seaweeds such as thongweed, this pipefish swims and hovers vertically. This provides an excellent camouflage, since the broad flattened snout and long body closely resemble the blade of a seagrass.

SIMILAR SPECIES: See comments on greater and Nilsson's pipefish.

KEY IDENTIFICATION FEATURES:

1. Long tubular body.

2. Broad, laterally
   compressed snout.

3. Polygonal in cross-section.

4. Dorsal, pectoral and tail
   fins present.

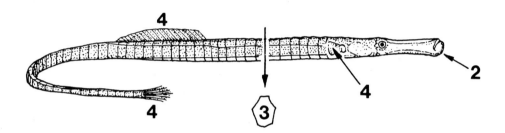

RED BAND-FISH *Cepola rubescens*

DESCRIPTION: Although a moderately common fish, the red band-fish has only been seen by divers at a very few sites (see below) since it mostly lives in deep water. It has a long, slender, eel-like body, flattened from side to side and tapering to a pointed tail. The dorsal and anal fins are long, extending for most of the length of the body. Since the fish lives in a mud burrow, the diver will normally only see the head with its large eyes and large oblique mouth peering out. However, with its beautiful red colouration, it is unlikely to be confused with anything else. The back is red to orange-red, and the belly is usually paler. The dorsal and anal fins in the male are golden-yellow, with a narrow, pale blue or violet margin which quickly fades out of water. In females the fins are much the same colour as the body. In both sexes there is a dark, vivid red area near the front of the dorsal fin.

SIZE: The maximum length is about 75cm, but 30–50cm is a more usual length.

DISTRIBUTION AND HABITAT: The exact distribution of this species is still not certain, but it has been recorded right up the west coast of Britain to Scotland, in the English Channel and all round Ireland. Most records are from dredgings from deep water of about 70–200m, but divers have now observed it off Lundy Island (Bristol Channel) and off Devon in as little as 10m of water. The fish live in club-shaped vertical burrows in muddy areas. The burrows have vertical entrances about 10cm across often with a pile of excavated material at one side.

76

BIOLOGY: The fish spawn in summer, at least in the English and Bristol Channels, but little else is known of their reproductive biology. In some instances a male and female fish have been observed sharing the same burrow, but whether this is usual is not yet known. The red band-fish appears to feed almost exclusively on small planktonic animals such as copepods, arrow worms (*Sagitta* sp.), fish eggs and ccrustacean larvae. It is thought that the fish remain in contact with their burrows when feeding, emerging just far enough to snap up any food items that swim or drift past them. However, there is also some indirect evidence that in some circumstances the fish may swim in mid-water. More diver observations are needed to ascertain whether this is so.

BEHAVIOUR: The fish spends most of its time in its burrow, and will soon withdraw into it if startled. A quiet approach and careful finning to avoid stirring up the mud are prerequisites for the diver who wants to see and photograph this fascinating fish. The question of whether the fish are more active by day or by night has not yet been fully resolved. The burrows of other animals, particularly the crab *Goniplax rhomboides*, have been found to connect with the red band-fish burrows, and this is probably a deliberate association.

SIMILAR SPECIES: There are no other similar species in European waters.

KEY IDENTIFICATION FEATURES:

1. Lives in mud burrows.

2. Long, flattened, red
   eel-like body.

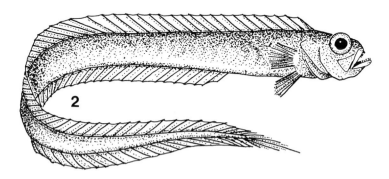

Lesser weaver.

LESSER WEEVER   *Echiichthys vipera*

GREATER WEEVER   *Trachinus draco*

DESCRIPTION: The name weever is derived from an Anglo-Saxon word meaning a viper, and reflects the venomous nature of these small fish. Weevers have a long body, with a deep but compressed head. They have mouths that point obliquely upwards and the eyes are on top of the head. On the back near to the head is a distinctive small fin, whose sharp spines have venom glands. Behind this is a much longer, second dorsal fin. The gill covers are also armed with smaller venomous spines. Both species are a sandy yellow-brown colour, the greater weever with characteristic dark diagonal streaks on the sides. Apart from size and habitat considerations, the two species can be distinguished by looking at the first dorsal fin, which is entirely black in the lesser weever, and only partly so in the greater weever. Similarly, the lesser weever has smoothly rounded pectoral fins, whilst these are more square-cut in the greater.

SIZE: The lesser weever is the smaller of the two, reaching only 15cm long (small hand size), whereas the greater weever reaches 40cm (hand plus forearm length).

DISTRIBUTION AND HABITAT: Weevers occur all round the coasts of Britain and Ireland, but only in sandy areas, and their distribution is patchy. Encounters with the greater weever are less likely, because it prefers deeper water from 30–100m, although in summer it appears to migrate inshore to spawn, and can be found as shallow as 5m or so. The lesser weever occurs down to about 50m, and often lives intertidally, moving in and out with the tide, and occasionally remaining on the shore, buried in the sand or in pools.

BIOLOGY: Little is known of the general biology of weevers. They spawn in the summer between June and August, the eggs floating freely in the plankton. They feed mainly on small, bottom-living animals, such as

78

amphipods (sand hoppers), brown shrimps, small crabs, worms, sand eels, dragonets and gobies. Lying camouflaged and partly buried in the sand during the day, they can quickly lunge upwards to catch passing fish. However, they are most active at night. Considerable research has been done on the sting, which appears to be entirely defensive, and is not used for catching prey. When erected, the black colour of the first dorsal fin shows up against the sand in which they live, and may serve as a warning. Danger to bathers and anyone on the beach comes from treading on the buried fish. Shrimp fishermen are often stung whilst sorting their catch, since at times, large numbers are caught in their nets. The sting is a nerve poison, and is intensely painful. However, it is not directly fatal, and no deaths have been recorded in Great Britain. The most widely recommended remedy is to soak the affected area in very hot water as soon as possible. The heat destroys the toxic quality of the venom. In spite of its sting, the greater weever is marketed as a food fish in Continental Europe, the head and poisonous dorsal fin being first removed.

BEHAVIOUR: Weevers spend most of the day lying buried in the sand with only the head and sometimes the first dorsal fin showing. At night they emerge and swim freely in search of food. The venomous first dorsal fin is only erected when danger threatens.

SIMILAR SPECIES: None in British waters.

KEY IDENTIFICATION FEATURES:

1. Oblique, upward-pointing mouth.

2. Small, spiny, black (lesser) or part black (greater) first dorsal fin; long second dorsal fin.

3. Pectoral fin smoothly rounded (lesser), square-cut (greater).

4. Oblique pattern of lines on sides (greater).

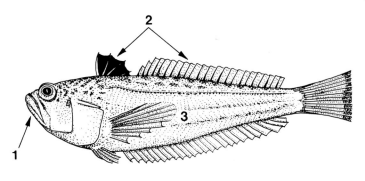

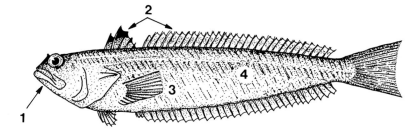

Sandeels.

SANDEEL   *Amodytes tobianus*

GREATER SANDEEL
Hyperoplus lanceolatus

DESCRIPTION: Sandeels are fish which almost every diver will encounter at some time, but which are difficult to approach close enough to identify. The diver usually sees them as shimmering shoals of small, silvery eel-like fish, or as groups of silver streaks swimming a metre or two above a sandy seabed. They have long, thin bodies, with a pointed jaw, a single long dorsal fin, and an anal fin about half the length of the dorsal. The small tail fin is distinctly forked. The belly and lower sides are silver, giving an overall silvery appearance, but the back and top sides are a bluish-green to yellowish-green. It is very difficult to tell the species apart under water. The greater sandeel is larger, and individuals over 20cm long are likely to be this species. Both species have highly protrusible mouths, but only the sandeel can protrude the top jaw as well as the bottom.

80

SIZE: The greater sandeel can reach 32cm long (forearm length), whilst the sandeel reaches only 20cm.

DISTRIBUTION AND HABITAT: Both species are widely distributed all round Britain and Ireland over clean sandy bottoms. The sandeel is extremely common, and is found from the shore down to about 30m. The less common greater sandeel extends deeper to 150m or so.

BIOLOGY: Sandeels lay their eggs mostly in spring and summer amongst the sand over which they live, and the eggs stick to the sand grains. Each female can produce between about 4,000–20,000 eggs. These hatch a few weeks later, and the tiny larval fish, only a few millimetres long, move out of the sand and live in the water column. The life span is several years – about 4 in the sandeel. They feed on small planktonic animals floating in the water, and on worms, small crustaceans and small fish. The greater sandeel even eats the smaller sandeel. Sandeels form a very important part of the diet of larger fish, many of them commercial species such as cod, herring, salmon, bass and mackerel. They are exploited commercially, using fine-meshed trawls, and are mostly processed into fish meal.

BEHAVIOUR: Sandeel shoals often swim in a head-down posture, and when danger threatens they dive down into the sand and immediately disappear. The schools are very well co-ordinated, and difficult to approach.

SIMILAR SPECIES: Three other sandeel species occur round Britain, but these mostly live below about 30m. The diver will rarely, if ever, be able to distinguish the different species underwater.

KEY IDENTIFICATION FEATURES:

1. Small, silvery, eel-like fish.

2. Forked tails.

3. Swim in shoals over sand.

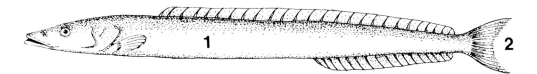

SNAKE BLENNY
Lumpenus lampretaeformis

DESCRIPTION: The snake blenny is related to the somewhat similar Yarrell's blenny (*Chirolophis ascani*) but is described here because of its suspected burrowing habit. As its name implies, this rather rarely-seen fish has a very long, slender body, with a single, long spiny dorsal and anal fin. The dorsal fin dips down at both the front and the back, the tail fin is long and pointed, and the pelvic fins soft and slender. Unlike Yarrell's blenny, it has no head tentacles. The colour varies from a pale brown to pale green or pale bluish with irregular brown blotches on the sides.

SIZE: The maximum length is about 49cm, but round the British Isles, it rarely reaches more than 25cm (forearm length).

82

DISTRIBUTION AND HABITAT: Essentially a northern species, the snake blenny is most common around Scotland. It does not extend into southern England or southern Ireland. It lives mostly in rather deep water from about 30–200m, and so is not often seen by divers. Most records come from the small numbers caught in trawls and the occasional large catches usually made in late spring in British waters. Like the red band fish (*Cepola rubescens*), it is thought to live in burrows in the mud, but this has yet to be observed.

BIOLOGY: The snake blenny spawns near the sea-bed in December and January. The young fish are pelagic, and are distributed by the water currents. They take up life on the sea-bed when about 3 months old. The diet consists mainly of small crustaceans, worms, brittlestars and molluscs that it can find in the mud. In turn, it is eaten by bottom-feeding fish such as cod and halibut.

SIMILAR SPECIES: Similar in shape to the butterfish (*Pholis gunnellus*), but this has distinctive markings and lives in a different habitat. Also similar to the viviparous blenny (*Zoarces viviparus*), but in this species the tail fin is continuous with the dorsal and anal fins. Yarrell's blenny (*Chirolophis ascani*) has large head tentacles.

KEY IDENTIFICATION FEATURES:

1. Eel-like body.

2. Long dorsal fin, low at
   front.

3. Pointed tail fin.

4. No head tentacle.

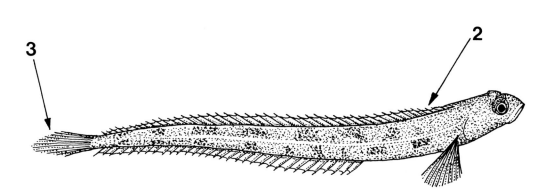

Section II. Hard sea-beds (rocky areas and wrecks)

FISH LIVING in rocky areas can be divided into two main groups; firstly there are the fish that live on the sea-bed itself, and are closely associated with it; secondly there are fish that are always or usually found in the vicinity of rocky reefs and wrecks, but which swim around freely in the open water. The second group are more loosely associated with the rock, and this group cannot be separated absolutely from the true open-water fish included in section III. Included here in the first group are: topknots, one of the very few flatfish to live on rocks; clinging fish such as the lumpsucker, sea-snails and clingfish which can grip firmly onto the rock even in rough water; gobies and blennies which make full use of cracks and crevices as permanent or semi-permanent homes; sea-scorpions, pipefish and sticklebacks that shelter in the dense undergrowth; eels and eel-like fish such as rocklings that can slither with ease in and out of the rocks or set up home in deep crevices and holes.

Fish in the second group spend their time swimming or hovering amongst the rocks and seaweeds searching for food, sheltering from predators, or apparently just passing the time of day. Some, like the wrasses, are dependent on the rocks for nesting sites and even for somewhere to sleep at night. Others, such as cod, are much more independent, and can also be found in open water and over sediments. Included here in this group, as well as the wrasses and the cod, are other cod-like fish such as pollack and bib, the John dory, two-spot gobies and sea-bream.

The variety and numbers of fish living in rocky areas is much greater than for sediment areas. Rock provides a wider variety of places to live, hide, lay eggs and build nests, as well as a wider variety of food items. Extensive growths of seaweeds and plant-like animals such as sea-firs, sea-mats, sponges and sea-squirts, provide shelter for a variety of smaller fish and for many of the animals on which they feed, such as worms, crustaceans and molluscs. Shipwrecks with their wide variety of hidey holes, surfaces, shapes, and often thick cover of attached and encrusting animals and seaweeds, seem to provide an irresistible attraction for fish, and are excellent places to go fish watching. A wreck sunk in a sandy or muddy area provides an artificial oasis for rock dwelling animals and fish, and compared with the surrounding sediment, will teem with life.

The distinction between fish that live on and around soft sea-beds and those that live on and around hard sea-beds is not absolute. There are many areas of mixed sand and rock where both groups can be found and there are many free swimming mobile fish that are just as happy searching for food over rock or sand.

TOPKNOT *Zeugopterus punctatus*

DESCRIPTION: The topknots are the only group of flatfish that habitually live in rocky areas rather than on sediment. Also, in contrast to most other flatfish, they are left-eyed. That is, if the fish is visualised swimming upright, then both eyes are on the left side of the body. The only other left-eyed flatfish at all likely to be seen by divers are brill, turbot, and scaldfish, and these all live on sediments. The topknot has a broad body with a large head. The dorsal fin starts very far forward, right on the snout, and both the dorsal and anal fins continue right back under the tail. It can easily be distinguished from the other two topknots by its distinctive markings. The basic colour is a warm brown with irregular dark blotches. Running from each eye to the edges of the body is a wide, dark stripe, and there is always a large dark blotch behind the pectoral fin near the middle of the body.

SIZE: Reaches about 25cm long (forearm length).

DISTRIBUTION AND HABITAT: The topknot has been found all round Great Britain and Ireland, except for the east coast of England, where little suitable habitat exists. It is fairly common, but sightings by divers are not frequent because the fish have the habit of clinging to the bottoms and sides of large rocks, and are difficult to spot. They live only in rocky areas or on rough ground, from very shallow water down to 30–40m. Young fish can be found on the lower shore on boulders in the kelp (*Laminaria*) zone.

BIOLOGY: Little is known of the biology of this non-commercial flatfish. It spawns in late winter to early spring, and the eggs and fry are probably planktonic. The diet has been very little studied, but probably consists of worms, crustaceans, and small fish that live amongst the undergrowth and seaweed on the rocks.

BEHAVIOUR: Once spotted, topknots can be closely approached and photographed, because they remain quite still, relying on their blotchy colour to provide them with camouflage.

SIMILAR SPECIES: Topknots are the only group of flatfish that live permanently in rocky areas. However, the lemon sole (*Microstomus kitt*) is sometimes found on rocks. It is a right-eyed flatfish.

KEY IDENTIFICATION FEATURES:

1. Lives on rock.

2. Distinctive markings.

3. Eyes on left side of body.

4. Fins extend right round body.

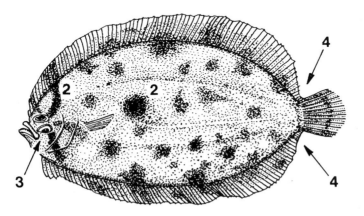

*Norwegian topknot (left)
and Eckstrom's topnot.*

NORWEGIAN TOPKNOT
Phrynorhombus norvegicus

ECKSTROM'S or BLOCH'S TOPKNOT
Phrynorhombus regius

DESCRIPTION: These two topknots are not always easy to distinguish in the field, since they do not have such distinctive markings as the topknot (*Zeugopterus*). However, they can often be closely approached and examined in detail. Like the topknot, both are left-eyed flatfish, and when found on rock, this should distinguish them from other flatfish. The Norwegian topknot is oval in shape and much more slender than Eckstrom's topknot, and has a smooth snout. Eckstrom's topknot has a distinct notch in the snout in front of the upper eye, and just behind this is the elongated first ray of the dorsal fin. The colour of the two species is similar, and is brownish, with irregular dusky patches. When living on rocks covered in the pink, encrusting seaweed, *Lithothamnion*, both species have been observed to have irregular pink markings. Eckstrom's topknot usually has one distinct, dark blotch, sometimes with a lighter centre on the mid-line towards the tail. If a close examination is possible, then the size of the scales is a useful diagnostic feature. These are large and obvious in the Norwegian topknot, and much smaller and less distinct in Eckstrom's topknot.

SIZE: The Norwegian topknot is the smallest of the topknots, reaching only 12cm (large palm size). Eckstrom's topknot can reach 20cm (large hand length).

DISTRIBUTION AND HABITAT: Both these species are found only on the Atlantic coasts of Britain. That is, around the south-west peninsula and up the west coast to Shetland, and all round Ireland. Like the topknot (*Zeugopterus*) they live amongst rocks and on rough grounds, and may have the same habit of clinging to the sides and undersides of rocks but this has not yet been observed by divers. Eckstrom's topknot can also

88

sometimes be found in shallow, sandy bays, especially where pebbles and stones abound. The Norwegian topknot is moderately common, Eckstrom's topknot less so, but sightings of either species by divers are not frequent. They can be found in water as shallow as 5m or so down to 50m, and in some areas much deeper.

BIOLOGY: Like the topknot, relatively little is known of the biology of these two species. They breed in the late spring and summer, and the eggs and very young fish float in the plankton. Young Norwegian topknot can be found on the bottom at a length of 13mm. Their food consists of small, bottom-living animals such as worms, crustaceans, and small fish.

SIMILAR SPECIES: See comments on Topknot (*Zeugopterus punctatus*).

KEY IDENTIFICATION FEATURES:

1. Live on rocks.

2. Eyes on left side of body.

3. Notch in snout (Eckstrom's).

4. Dark blotch on side (Eckstrom's).

5. Large scales (Norwegian).

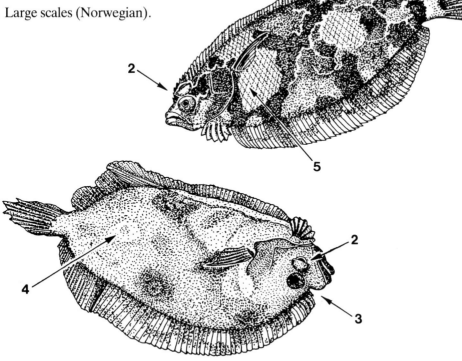

LUMPSUCKER or SEA HEN
Cyclopterus lumpus

DESCRIPTION: The slightly grotesque lumpsucker is an easy fish to recognise. It has a large, rounded body, covered in bony plates which stick out as hard lumps. Some of these plates are enlarged and arranged in rows along the sides of the body. The pelvic fins form a large sucker disc on the belly, with which the fish clings firmly onto the rocks. Adults appear to have only one dorsal fin near the tail. However, there are really two, and these can be seen clearly in juveniles. In adults the first fin becomes gradually overgrown and hidden by thick skin. Most lumpsuckers are a bluish-grey or greenish-brown, with a paler underside. In the breeding season, males develop an orange or reddish colour over the belly and up the sides. The juveniles are green.

SIZE: Females can reach 60cm, whilst males usually reach only 50cm. However, most adults are between 25cm and 40cm (forearm length and forearm plus hand length).

90

DISTRIBUTION AND HABITAT: The lumpsucker is common all round the coasts of Britain and Ireland. Adults of breeding age live on the bottom among rocks from low water mark to at least 200m. They can be found in areas pounded by strong waves, because they can cling onto the rocks with their powerful sucker. Larvae and juveniles are planktonic, and young fish can be found attached to floating seaweed or debris. Non-breeding adults can also live in deep, open water, but too deep to be seen by divers. Young fish can be found in low tide rock pools.

BIOLOGY: In spring, between February and about May, the lumpsucker comes inshore to spawn, and it is at this time that divers are most likely to see them. The female lays her loose masses of pink, brown, red or pale yellow eggs in shallow water often just above low spring tide mark between rocks and in crevices. Each mass contains up to 136,000 eggs. She then returns to deeper water, leaving the male to guard the eggs. He does this with great vigour, rarely leaving the nest, and removing any marauding crabs, starfish or molluscs. He also fans the eggs with his fins and pushes his head into the clump of spawn to keep them well oxygenated until they hatch one to two months later and the larvae disperse into the plankton. During this time the males are vulnerable to attack by seabirds at low tide. They are also eaten by other fish such as halibut and angler fish, and by otters and seals. During spring storms, large numbers are sometimes washed ashore, particularly on the North Sea coast, having been unable to keep their grip on the rocks in the violent wave surge. The lumpsucker does not feed during the spawning migration, but its normal diet consists mainly of bottom-living crustaceans, worms and fishes. Although not commercially important, some numbers of lumpfish are caught for their roe, which is sold as a substitute caviar.

BEHAVIOUR: Male lumpfish can often be closely approached when guarding their clump of eggs. Diver observations suggest that some nest sites are used year after year, probably by the same fish, and some individuals certainly have home sites where they can regularly be seen.

SIMILAR SPECIES: Sea-snails (*Liparis* spp.) and clingfish also have their pelvic fins modified to form suckers, but they are much smaller, and do not have bony plates on the body by which even juvenile lumpsuckers can be easily recognised.

KEY IDENTIFICATION FEATURES:

1. Bony plates/lumps on body.

2. Large sucker on belly.

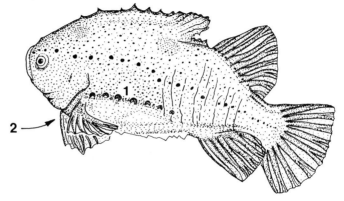

Montagu's sea snail.

SEA-SNAIL *Liparis liparis*

MONTAGU'S SEA-SNAIL
Liparis montagui

DESCRIPTION: Sea-snails are small, clinging fish, closely related to the much larger lumpsucker. The two species are difficult to tell apart in the field, but one is primarily a shore dweller and one lives only below the shore (see below). They have almost tadpole-shaped bodies, with a broad, smooth head. Underneath, they have a rounded sucker derived from the pelvic fins, with which they can cling firmly to rocks and seaweed. They have a single, long dorsal fin, and a long anal fin. In the sea-snail these are both joined to the tail fin, whilst in Montagu's sea-snail they are not. However, this is not easy to see under water. Sea-snails have no scales, and their skin is loose, soft and a bit slimy, which is probably the origin of their rather strange name. The skin is actually covered in minute prickles,

92

but these cannot easily be seen. The colour is a poor guide to identity, since it is variable with the habitat. Many are a drab brown but they can be yellowish, reddish or greenish.

SIZE: The sea-snail is the larger of the two, usually up to 12cm long (large palm size). Montagu's sea-snail usually reaches only half this size, but some can reach 9cm.

DISTRIBUTION AND HABITAT: Both these fish have a wide distribution, and can commonly be found all round Great Britain and Ireland. However, Montagu's sea-snail has not been recorded from the south-east coast of England around the East Anglian bulge. The sea-snail is usually found in shallow water, but extends down to at least 150m. It does not live on the shore, but is common in estuaries. It is sometimes found in muddy and sandy areas, but lives mainly amongst rocks. Montagu's sea-snail is mostly found on the shore in pools and under seaweed. However, it is not confined to the shore, which increases the difficulty of distinguishing the two species under water.

BIOLOGY: The sea-snail lays its eggs in winter, and Montagu's sea-snail in spring to early summer. Both species attach their eggs in small clumps to seaweeds (especially to the holdfasts), hydroids (sea-firs), and bushy bryozoa (sea-mats). They hatch after a few weeks, and the larval fish drift away in the plankton. Those that survive and complete their development settle down onto the seabed when they are about 1cm or so long. Montagu's sea-snail appears to feed only on small crustaceans, whereas the sea-snail also eats worms and small fish, perhaps because of its larger size.

BEHAVIOUR: Sea-snails spend much of their time firmly attached to a rock or seaweed. The grip of their sucker is quite powerful, and they are difficult to remove. Since they rely on their cryptic colour for camouflage, divers may find it possible to approach close enough to try to move them. On the shore these fish are most likely to be found curled up, clinging to the underside of a rock.

SIMILAR SPECIES: The clingfishes are another group of small fish that cling to rocks with a sucker, but they are clearly different in body shape and fin arrangement.

KEY IDENTIFICATION FEATURES:

1. Sucker on underside.

2. Tadpole shape; one long dorsal fin.

3. Soft, loose skin.

4. Dorsal and anal fins joined to tail fin (sea-snail) or not (Montagu's sea-snail).

Shore clingfish (left) and Connemara clingfish.

SHORE CLINGFISH or CORNISH SUCKER *Lepadogaster lepadogaster*

CONNEMARA CLINGFISH *Lepadogaster candollei*

DESCRIPTION: Clingfish are small fish which, as their name suggests, cling firmly to rocks by means of a powerful sucker formed partly from the pelvic fins. Four species are found in British waters, of which the shore and Connemara clingfish are the largest. These clingfish have flattened, almost triangular heads, with a long snout that looks rather like a duck's bill. The body is also flattened, but sideways not downwards. There is only one dorsal fin, set well back towards the tail. In the shore clingfish, the dorsal and anal fins are joined to the tail fin, whilst in the Connemara clingfish, they are not. Another difference is that the shore clingfish has a fringed "tentacle" just in front of the eye, whilst the Connemara clingfish has only a small flap of skin. However, given the small size of these fish, this may be difficult to see under water. The colour of both these fish is variable from reddish and brownish to greenish and yellowish, with various spots and stripes. However, the shore clingfish always has a pair of bright blue spots rimmed with yellow, red, or black on the back, just behind the head. Large Connemara clingfish have three red spots at the base of the dorsal fin, and others on the head.

SIZE: Similar in size, the maximum length is about 7–8cm (index finger size).

94

DISTRIBUTION AND HABITAT: Both species are found only on the west and south-west coasts of Britain and around Ireland. As its name suggests, the shore clingfish lives on the shore, and is most likely to be seen by rock pool enthusiasts. At times, and in some localities, it can be quite abundant. The Connemara clingfish can be found on the lower shore, but also extends down to at least 30m, living amongst kelp, seagrass and stones. It is comparatively rarely recorded.

BIOLOGY: The eggs of both species are laid in summer, and are attached to the undersides of rocks. They are guarded by one of the parents until they hatch. The young fish float in the plankton for a short while until development is complete and they can settle down to a life on the seabed. Little is known about what these fish eat.

BEHAVIOUR: These small fish spend much of their time clinging to the undersides of rocks, and so are not often seen unless specifically searched for.

SIMILAR SPECIES: See two-spotted clingfish and small-headed clingfish. Sea-snails (*Liparis* spp.) also cling to rocks with a sucker, but are easily distinguished from clingfish.

KEY IDENTIFICATION FEATURES:

1. Sucker on the underside.

2. Duck-bill shaped snout.

3. One dorsal and anal fin both attached to tail fin (shore) or unattached (Connemara).

4. Pair of blue spots behind head (shore).

5. Red spots on head and base of dorsal fin (Connemara).

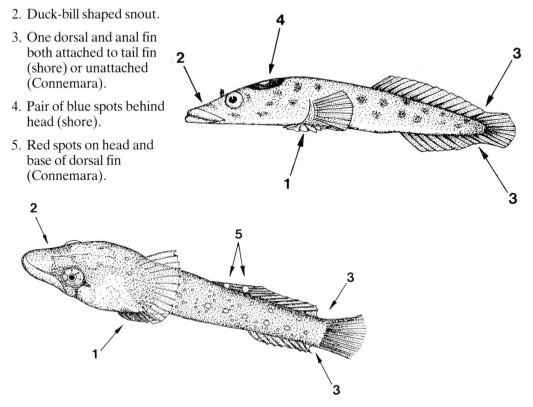

Two-spotted clingfish.

TWO-SPOTTED CLINGFISH
Diplecogaster bimaculata

SMALL-HEADED CLINGFISH
Apletodon microcephalus

DESCRIPTION: These two small clingfish are similar in shape to the larger shore and Connemara clingfish. However, they have such shorter heads, and rounded snouts without the duck-billed appearance of the larger species. Underneath, they have the small, powerful sucker characteristic of clingfish. There is a single dorsal and anal fin, both set far back near the tail. These fins are much shorter than in the larger clingfish, and in neither species are they joined to the tail fin. The two species are very difficult to tell apart, even out of the water, and it is often necessary to look at the teeth – hardly practical underwater! However, the male two-spotted clingfish can be distinguished because he has a characteristic purple spot, outlined with yellow, behind each pectoral fin (note that the similar spots of the shore clingfish, (*L. lepadogaster*), are in a different position just behind the eyes. The basic colour of both species is variable, and of limited use in identification. The two-spotted clingfish is often a patchy reddish colour on the back, and yellowish ventrally, with variously coloured spots. The small-headed clingfish is often reddish-brown or greenish-brown, with lighter patches and spots. The males may have a purple patch on the throat, and the females a pale patch.

96

SIZE: The maximum size of both species is 4–5cm (little finger size).

DISTRIBUTION AND HABITAT: The two-spotted clingfish is moderately common all round the coasts of Great Britain and Ireland, except that on the east coast it has only been recorded from isolated spots near St. Abbs. The small-headed clingfish has been recorded from the west coast of Great Britain, the English Channel and all round Ireland. It may be more widespread, and more records from divers are needed. Both species can be found from the lower shore down to 25m for the small-headed species, and 55m for the two-spotted species. They are found mostly in rocky and stony areas, but can also be common in seagrass beds and other sediment areas where there are plenty of empty mollusc shells to provide shelter.

BIOLOGY: The two-spotted clingfish lays its eggs in spring and summer on the underside of a shell or under stones, and these are guarded by the parents, mostly the male. After hatching, the larval fish live in the plankton before settling down on the seabed during the autumn. Less is known of the biology of the small-headed species, but it probably follows a similar pattern. It lays its eggs within the holdfasts of kelp and other large seaweeds, and the young are found amongst seaweeds in the autumn. The two-spotted clingfish feeds mainly on small crustaceans.

BEHAVIOUR: These little fish are difficult to spot under water, but can sometimes be found by turning over shells and stones. The author has occasionally found them sheltering right inside the hollow holdfasts of the furbellows kelp, *Sacchoriza polyschides*.

SIMILAR SPECIES: See shore clingfish and Connemara clingfish. Sea-snails (*Liparis* spp.) also cling to rocks with a sucker, but are easily distinguished from clingfish.

KEY IDENTIFICATION FEATURES:

1. Sucker on underside.

2. One short dorsal and anal fin.

3. Yellow-rimmed purple spot behind pectoral fin (male two-spotted).

LEOPARD SPOTTED GOBY
Thorogobius ephippiatus
(= Gobius forsteri)

DESCRIPTION: Gobies are notoriously difficult to identify underwater, but the dramatically-coloured leopard spotted goby is an exception. It is typically goby shaped, with characteristic thick lips, close-set eyes near the top of the head, and two dorsal fins. The colouration is an unmistakable pale fawn, with conspicuous orange, brick-red or blackish blotches all over the head and body – hence the common name. There is also a black spot on the rear part of the first dorsal fin, and some individuals have a whitish edge to the dorsal and anal fins.

SIZE: This is a large goby, reaching a maximum size of 13cm (palm size).

98

DISTRIBUTION AND HABITAT: The leopard spotted goby was originally thought to be extremely rare and rather restricted in distribution. It was only occasionally caught in the traps and nets of biologists and fishermen. However, in recent years diver observations have shown that it is widespread around the coasts of Britain and Ireland, but is shy by nature, and lives in steep, rocky areas that are difficult to sample. So far it has been recorded on all our coasts except the east coast of Britain south of St. Abbs. This is probably due to a lack of suitable habitat in this area, since it lives mainly in crevices in vertical or steep rock faces. A diver will typically see individuals sitting on small ledges in front of their home crevices, or at the bases of large, stable boulder blocks, where suitable crevices are available. They do not mind a certain amount of silt on the rock surface, and are found in sheltered estuaries and sea-lochs as well as on the open coast, provided suitable habitat is available. The depth distribution is from low water of spring tides to about 40m, but individuals are occasionally found in rock pools.

BIOLOGY: Relatively little is as yet known about the biology of this beautiful goby. It is thought to spawn between May to July in the English Channel, but most observations have been made on captive fish. It feeds mainly on small amphipod crustaceans (sand hoppers) and worms. Diver observations on all aspects of breeding, territorial and feeding behaviour would be useful.

BEHAVIOUR: Unlike many of the other gobies and blennies, the leopard spotted goby is very shy and retiring. The diver is most likely to spot them on night dives, since they are to some extent nocturnal. They can be seen during the day, especially on deeper (and therefore darker) dives. Unless approached quietly, they quickly disappear into the protection of their home crevices. Some divers have reported slight colour changes at night.

SIMILAR SPECIES: No other British goby has similar markings.

KEY IDENTIFICATION FEATURES:

1. Dark leopard-like blotches.

2. Crevice/ledge habitat.

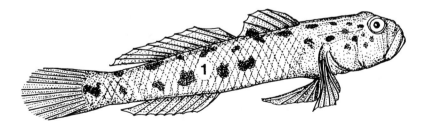

ROCK GOBY   *Gobius paganellus*

DESCRIPTION: The rock goby has few distinguishing features, but any moderately large goby living amongst rocks on or just below the shore is most likely to be this species. In colour it is a mottled brown or purple brown to almost black. However, the first dorsal fin always has a pale band along the upper edge, which becomes a conspicuous orange in adult males. This can only be clearly seen when the two dorsal fins are erect. A close examination might show finger-like branches around the nostrils.

SIZE: This is a large goby, reaching 12cm in length (palm sized).

DISTRIBUTION AND HABITAT: The rock goby has so far been found only on the western and southern coasts of Britain and all round Ireland. As its name suggests, it is confined to rocky areas, which may in part explain its apparent absence from the east coast, where such habitats are scarce. It is perhaps more likely to be seen by snorkellors than by divers, since it is mostly found on shores, hiding under stones and seaweeds and in rock pools. It also lives in shallow water down to about 15m.

BIOLOGY: Like other gobies, the rock goby lays its eggs under rocks and in crevices. The eggs are attached by one end to the roof of the crevice, and are closely packed, in a single layer. This happens between April and June in British waters. This goby is a very unfussy feeder and will eat almost anything, including young fish, small crustaceans, and small pieces of seaweed. Surprisingly, it is thought to live for up to 10 years.

BEHAVIOUR: This fish leads a generally solitary life, and individuals can often be seen sitting quietly on the tops of rocks, surveying their territories.

SIMILAR SPECIES: The giant goby (*Gobius cobitis*) is also found in rock pools and is similar in overall appearance. It grows to a much larger size (27cm) and has a very restricted distribution in the western Channel. See also the black goby (*Gobius niger*).

KEY IDENTIFICATION FEATURES:

1. Pale yellow or orange band
   at top of first dorsal fin.

2. Finger-like branches
   around anterior nostril
   (difficult to see).

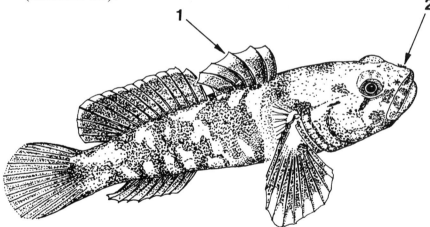

TOMPOT BLENNY
Parablennius gattorugine
(= Blennius gattorugine)

DESCRIPTION: The tompot is a rather stout blenny, with a deep head and a large, much-branched tentacle above each eye. The single, long dorsal fin has only a very shallow notch between the spiny front half and the soft-rayed back half. The colour is often a reddish-brown, but can also be other shades of brown, and there is always a series of 7 or more jagged dark brown bars running vertically from the dorsal fin to the belly.

SIZE: The maximum size is 30cm, but most are less than 20cm (large hand length).

DISTRIBUTION AND HABITAT: The tompot is common on north, west and south coasts of Britain, and all round Ireland, but is not found in the North Sea, and therefore not on the east coast. It is particularly common in the east part of the English Channel. It lives amongst rocks, and can be found hiding on rock ledges and amongst seaweed, where it is

102

particularly well camouflaged. It also inhabits cobble and boulder areas. Divers commonly encounter the tompot with its head sticking out from little hidey-holes in wrecks, and some even make their homes in wide-necked bottles and old tin cans. Yarrel's blenny also frequents wrecks, but a blenny with its tentacled head sticking out of a hole watching you is almost certainly a tompot. It lives mostly in the immediate subtidal zone, from about 1 to 12m, but can sometimes be found deeper and also in rock pools.

BIOLOGY: The female tompot lays her eggs between mid-March to April in a rock crevice or similar hiding place. The male then fertilises the eggs and guards them, keeping them well oxygenated by fanning a current of water over them. The eggs hatch after about a month and the free swimming larvae are thought to settle back down on the bottom by about the middle of summer. Just what the tompot eats has not been fully worked out, but the diet seems to consist mainly of small crustaceans, for which it hunts amongst the seaweeds and rocks.

BEHAVIOUR: Apart from the goldsinny wrasse, the tompot must rate as one of the cheekiest and most inquisitive of British fish. As long as the diver makes no sudden movements, they can be closely approached, and will often come out of their hidey-holes to see what is going on. They have a habit of propping themselves up on the two spines of their pelvic fins in order to get a better view.

SIMILAR SPECIES: Montagu's, Butterfly and Yarrell's blennies all have large head tentacles, but are easily distinguished by other features such as colouration and by reference to their habitat and distribution.

KEY IDENTIFICATION FEATURES:

1. Large branched tentacle
   above each eye.

2. Dark bars across the body.

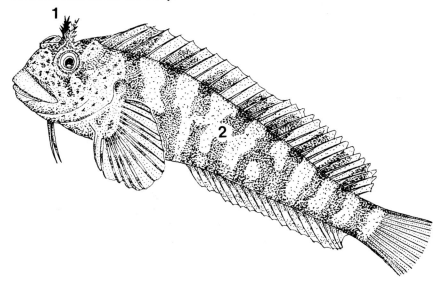

SHANNY
Lipophrys pholis (= Blennius pholis)

DESCRIPTION: The shanny can readily be distinguished from other blennies because it does not have a tentacle on top of the head. It has all the other characteristics typical of blennies, and its thick lips and eyes set high up on the head give it a faintly comical look. Most shannies have a smoothly-rounded profile, but larger, older fish show their age by developing a fleshy ridge on the forehead. The single, long dorsal fin has a shallow notch at about the halfway point. Shannies exhibit a wide range of colours, and are experts at camouflage. Individuals living amongst dark seaweeds and rocks may be a dull brown, whilst olive green fish will be found amongst green seaweeds. The colour is usually rather blotchy, and there is a rather indistinct dark spot on the front of the dorsal fin. During breeding the males tend to become very dark. Like the butterfish, the shanny has a slimy, scaleless skin, and is very difficult to get hold of.

104

SIZE: Adults can grow to as much as 16cm long (hand length).

DISTRIBUTION AND HABITAT: The shanny is one of the most widespread of all British inshore fish. It is very common all round the coasts of Britain and Ireland, and lives in a variety of habitats. It is very adaptable, and so is often found around man-made structures such as pier pilings, jetties, and shipwrecks. It is most common onshore in rock pools right up to the level of high water of neap tides. It can also be found on muddy and sandy shores in pools with stones in the bottom and seaweed under which to hide. So it is most likely to be seen by snorkellors and sea shore walkers, but it does also live down to a depth of 30m or so.

BIOLOGY: In common with most other blennies and gobies, the male shanny is a very attentive parent. Spawning occurs throughout the spring and summer, and the female attaches the eggs to the roof of a crevice or the underside of a large stone. The male then guards the eggs until they hatch up to two months after laying. During this time he makes sure they have plenty of oxygen by fanning them with his pectoral fins. The shanny will eat almost anything it can catch, but lives mostly on small crabs and other crustaceans. The young have the interesting habit of nipping off the legs of barnacles as they are extended for feeding.

BEHAVIOUR: This bold little fish has the typical blenny habit of propping itself up on its pelvic fins and looking all round. Provided no sudden movements are made, it will remain out in the open, watching the watcher. However, with eyes set high on its head, it has very acute vision, and will rapidly dart away if danger threatens. In winter, the shanny tends to move off the shore, and lives below the low water mark, where it is less exposed to winter storms.

SIMILAR SPECIES: There should be no confusion with other true blennies, since all the others have tentacles on top of their heads. The viviparous "blenny" and the snake "blenny" do not have tentacles, but these are not true blennies, and are easily distinguished by their elongated shape.

KEY IDENTIFICATION FEATURES:

1. No tentacles on the head.

2. Single long dorsal fin.

3. Dark spot on front of dorsal fin (may be indistinct).

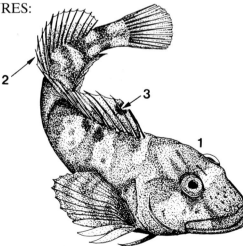

MONTAGU'S BLENNY
Coryphoblennius galerita
(= Blennius galerita and
Blennius montagui)

DESCRIPTION: This is a small blenny not often seen by divers, but one which is readily recognised. Instead of two separate head tentacles, as seen in other blennies, it has a characteristic fleshy crest, which runs between the eyes. The top edge of this crest has a fringe of short filaments. In the middle of the head behind the crest a row of small fine tentacles runs backwards. The single, long dorsal fin has a conspicuous notch in the middle. The colour also helps identification because most individuals are covered in small blue-white spots on an olive or greeny-brown background. In males the fringe of the head crest is yellow, and the corner of the mouth is orange or yellow.

106

SIZE: Adults only grow to about 8.5cm (about as long as a finger).

DISTRIBUTION AND HABITAT: Montagu's blenny is only found around south-west Britain and the southern half of Ireland. It is a shore fish which lives in rock pools at about mid-tide level, rarely as far down the shore as the kelp (*Laminaria*) zone. It does not like a lot of weed cover, and is commonest in fairly bare pools or those in which the pink seaweed *Corallina* is growing. It is therefore not often seen by divers.

BIOLOGY: In common with other blennies, the eggs are laid in rock crevices, usually attached to the ceiling, and are guarded by the male until they hatch. In Britain, the eggs are laid in July. Like the young of the shanny, this little blenny feeds mainly on the limbs of barnacles, which are bitten off when they are extended for feeding. It also eats copepods (small planktonic crustaceans).

BEHAVIOUR: Little other information available.

SIMILAR SPECIES: The key identification features outlined above and the restricted distribution should make this blenny easy to identify.

KEY IDENTIFICATION FEATURES:

1. Single fringed fleshy flap
   between the eyes.

2. Row of small tentacles on
   top of the head.

3. Deep notch in dorsal fin.

4. Blue-white spots.

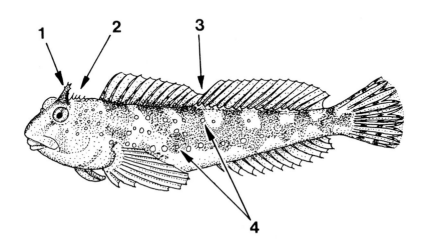

YARRELL'S BLENNY *Chirolophis ascani*

DESCRIPTION: A long, slender blenny with a single, un-notched, spiny dorsal fin running the length of the body. The first few spines of this fin are tufted at the tips. On top of the head there are a number of small filaments and there is also a large branched tentacle above each eye. The colouration is a yellowish or greenish brown, with distinctly darker vertical bars running across the body and the dorsal fin. There is a dark ring around the eye which extends downwards across the cheek. Though closely resembling the true blennies (Blennidae), Yarrell's blenny belongs to a different group, the Arctic blennies (Stichaeidae).

108

SIZE: Up to 25cm (forearm length).

DISTRIBUTION AND HABITAT: Yarrell's blenny occurs round most of Britain and Ireland, but is only locally common, and is only spasmodically seen by divers. Most records from divers, come from Scotland, the Hebrides and Orkney because the species' main stronghold is further north in Scandinavia where it is much more common. It lives amongst rocks, usually in crevices, and mostly below about 20m. It is often found on wrecks which provide numerous hiding holes.

BIOLOGY: The eggs are laid on the seabed, and the young are found in the plankton between January to June depending on the latitude – those in the colder northern waters hatching later. Its food consists of small molluscs and worms, but little is really known about the biology. It is believed that the eggs are laid in crevices and guarded by an adult, but this has not been confirmed, and diver observations are needed.

BEHAVIOUR: This fish has the characteristic blenny habit of propping itself up on its small pelvic fins.

SIMILAR SPECIES: Tompot, Montagu's and Butterfly blennies also have large head tentacles but all are easily distinguished by colouration and the shape of the head tentacles. Montagu's blenny occurs only on the shore in the south and west.

KEY IDENTIFICATION FEATURES:

1. A large, branched tentacle above each eye.

2. Small filaments on head and first few dorsal fin spines.

3. Dark stripe across cheek beneath eye.

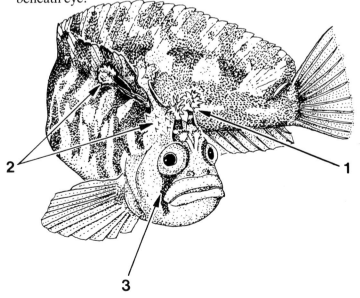

BUTTERFISH or GUNNEL
Pholis gunnellus

DESCRIPTION: The butterfish has a long, eel-like body, which is flattened from side to side. Picking up one of these fish is extremely difficult, since their mucous-covered skin makes them very slippery – hence the common name. It has only one dorsal fin running the whole length of the body, made up of short spines. The anal fin is about half the length of the dorsal. Most butterfish are a rather nondescript brown colour, with irregular, darker, vertical bars or a mottled pattern. However, this species is readily recognised by the distinct row of white-ringed black spots along the base of the dorsal fin. There are usually about 12 of these, but the number varies from 9 to 15. Small, raised black spots on the skin of some individuals are the cysts of a parasitic worm. Like the related Yarrell's blenny, the butterfish has a dark stripe running from below each eye to the corners of the mouth. Both these blennies belong to a group called the Arctic blennies (families Stichaeidae and Pholidae).

110

SIZE: The butterfish can reach 25cm (forearm length), but is very slow growing, and it is the smaller fish that are more often seen.

DISTRIBUTION AND HABITAT: This is a common fish all round the coast of Britain and Ireland. It lives mostly on rocky shores, and can be found hiding under rocks, amongst seaweed, and in rock pools. With its thin, slippery body, it is able to slip into very small crevices if danger threatens. However, it also lives in deeper water down to about 100m, and the diver will see it lying quietly hidden amongst seaweeds or animal growths on the rocks and in kelp holdfasts. It can sometimes also be found on sand and mud, hiding in empty shells or between loose pebbles.

BIOLOGY: Around Britain the female butterfish lays her eggs in January and February. She deposits sticky clumps of several hundred eggs between stones, in empty shells such as oysters, or in the holes made by boring molluscs in the rocks. She may also curl her body around the clump to compact it into a small brazil nut-sized ball. The eggs are guarded by the female, or sometimes alternately by both parents, until the eggs hatch about a month later. The young fish drift in the plankton for some time before settling down to a life on the seabed. They grow very slowly – between 1 to 3cm a year – and are thought to live for about 10 years. The butterfish feeds on small, slow-moving animals such as worms, molluscs and small crustaceans. In turn it forms an abundant food supply for other fish and seabirds, as well as fishing bait for small boys. How important an item of diet this abundant little fish is to other inshore species has not been well studied.

BEHAVIOUR: When approached, the butterfish will often remain still, perhaps relying on the row of white-rimmed "eyes" along its back to frighten predators. However, its smooth body and minute pelvic fins allow it to wriggle rapidly down between the rocks if necessary.

SIMILAR SPECIES: Eels and some blennies have a similar body shape, but the row of spots is unmistakable.

KEY IDENTIFICATION FEATURES:

1. Conspicuous spots along
   the base of the dorsal fin.

2. Eel-like body.

3. One long dorsal fin.

4. Black stripe through eye.

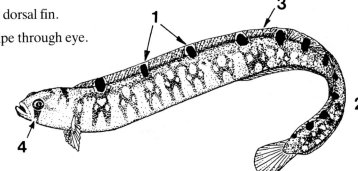

Long-spined sea scorpion (left) and bull rout.

BULL ROUT, FATHER LASHER or SHORT-SPINED SEA SCORPION
Myoxocephalus scorpius

LONG-SPINED SEA SCORPION
Taurulus bubalis

DESCRIPTION: Sea scorpions are stout, robust fish with a broad head, armed with sharp spines. They have no scales, but instead the fish is protected by hard, bony plates embedded in the skin. There are two dorsal fins, and in the first one the fin rays are sharp spines. The bull rout and long-spined sea scorpion are similar in overall appearance, and at first glance can easily be confused, especially when small. However, there is one simple way to tell them apart. The long-spined sea scorpion always has a small barbel at both corners of the mouth, whereas the bull rout does not. In small fish it is important to look closely for this. The long-spined sea scorpion, as its name suggests, has one very long, strong spine on the cheek, as well as a number of smaller ones, whereas the cheek spines in the bull rout are more equal in length. Both species have a spiny lateral line, but the bull rout also has small spines in the skin on either side of the line. The usual colour for both species is a mottled greeny-brown above, with a yellowish (*Taurulus*) to reddish (*Myoxocephalus*) belly. However, the long-spined sea scorpion can accurately adjust its colour to suit the background, and can be a deep red when living amongst red seaweeds, bright green when amongst the green algae of a shallow pool, or dark brown when hiding under bladder wrack.

SIZE: The bull rout is the larger of the two species, reaching 30cm (forearm length). The long-spined sea scorpion rarely exceeds 17.5cm (hand sized), and so large fish are likely to be the bull rout.

DISTRIBUTION AND HABITAT: These two bottom-living species are both widely distributed around the coasts of Great Britain and Ireland. The bull rout can be found on almost any type of seabed, including mud

112

and sand, as well as rock, from about 2m to 60m depth. It is very rarely found on the shore. The long-spined sea scorpion in contrast, appears to live only in rocky areas, especially amongst algae. It is a common shore inhabitant, but extends down to about 30m depth. Its mottled colour provides good camouflage and it is not always easy to spot.

BIOLOGY: The bull rout spawns in winter (December to March) and lays clumps of eggs between rocks. As its other name of father lasher suggests, the male guards the eggs until they hatch 5 to 12 weeks later, depending on the water temperature. The long-spined sea scorpion lays its eggs amongst seaweeds in early spring. It is uncertain whether there is parental care by this species. The young float in the plankton after hatching, returning to the seabed when they reach about 1½cm long. Both species feed mainly on bottom-living fish and crustaceans such as gobies, blennies, sand hoppers, shrimps, prawns and crabs. The bull rout probably has a more varied diet, since it ranges over a greater number of habitats. Though painful if trodden on or handled wrongly, sea scorpions (Cottidae) are not poisonous, unlike the similar scorpion fish (Scorpaenidae) found in the Mediterranean.

BEHAVIOUR: These fish are well camouflaged by their colouration, and protected by their sharp spines, and so will often remain quite still when approached by a diver.

SIMILAR SPECIES: The Norway bullhead (*Taurulus lilljeborgi*) is very similar to *Taurulus bubalis*. It mostly occurs in deep water below 20m around Scotland and the northern part of Ireland, and is not often seen by divers. Like *Taurulus bubalis*, it has a small barbel at the corner of the mouth, but unlike this species, it has a row of spines above the lateral line.

KEY IDENTIFICATION FEATURES:

1. Two dorsal fins.

2. *Taurulus* has a mouth barbel.

3. *Taurulus* has one very long spine on the cheek.

4. *Myoxocephalus* has numerous small spines in the skin, either side of the lateral line.

SNAKE PIPEFISH   *Entelurus aequoreus*

DESCRIPTION: The aptly named snake pipefish has a long, smooth, rounded body, which tapers to a thin tail with only a minute tail fin. It does not have the angular look and feel of the other large pipefish, and it has no pectoral fins. It can be immediately recognised by its beautiful colouration, even if only part of the body can be seen. The basic colour is a pale brown or yellowish-brown, but each body ring is marked by a thin, pale blue or sometimes silvery band, with slightly darker edges. There is also a reddish line running from the tip of the snout through the eye, back to the gill cover.

SIZE: Females of this species reach the largest size of all the pipefish found in British waters, attaining 60cm (an arm's length). Males reach only about 40cm.

DISTRIBUTION AND HABITAT: Although this species can be found all round the British Isles and Ireland, it is relatively rare, and is only occasionally reported by divers. Unlike the other large pipefish, it

114

lives mostly in rocky areas amongst kelp and other large seaweeds, commonly from about 10m to 30m depth. However, it does extend as deep as 100m, where there is unlikely to be any seaweed cover. In the summer it can also be found swimming at the surface, far out to sea, particularly amongst floating seaweed debris.

BIOLOGY: The snake pipefish follows the typical pipefish pattern of breeding, with the males carrying the eggs. The female lays several hundred eggs into the male's brood-pouch during early summer, and males carrying eggs are usually found in July and August. The male's pouch is not as well-developed as in the genus *Syngnathus* (e.g. greater pipefish) and is simply a hollow along the underside. The young are released when they are only about 1cm long, and they are not fully-developed. At this stage they have minute pectoral fins, but these soon disappear. The young drift in the plankton for a short while until their development is complete. The diet of this pipefish is not well known, but is likely to be similar to other pipefish, namely small floating crustaceans and fish fry.

BEHAVIOUR: Tends to remain hidden amongst seaweeds, but is not as well camouflaged as other species.

SIMILAR SPECIES: The colour clearly distinguishes it from other species. At sea, large specimens might be mistaken for true sea snakes, but these do not generally occur in British waters.

KEY IDENTIFICATION FEATURES:

1. Smooth snake-like body.

2. No obvious fins, apart from
   the dorsal.

3. Distinctive colouration.

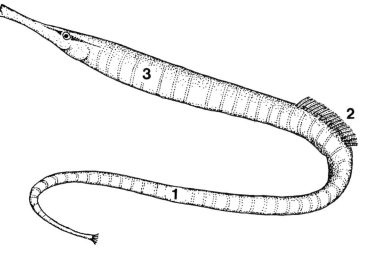

Worm pipefish.

WORM PIPEFISH
Nerophis lumbriciformis

STRAIGHT-NOSED PIPEFISH
Nerophis ophidion

DESCRIPTION: These two pipefish are both very slender, and have long, smooth, worm-like bodies, with no fins apart from a small dorsal fin. Their body segments are not obvious (as they are in the greater and other pipefish), and in cross-section they are rounded, not polygonal. The head and snout are relatively small. The best way to tell these two species apart in the field is to look at the snout. In the worm pipefish this is distinctly turned up, and as the name suggests, this is not so in the straight-nosed pipefish. There is also some difference in colour, size, and habitat. The worm pipefish is always a very dark colour – usually green or brown, blending in well with the background. It may have some lighter markings underneath. The straight-nosed pipefish is variable in colour – usually greeny-brown on the back with paler sides, and whitish green or yellow below. Females sometimes have long, bluish lines near the belly, and some fish have vertical rows of spots on the front half of the fish.

SIZE: The straight-nosed pipefish is the larger of the two species, reaching 30cm (about forearm length). The worm pipefish reaches about half this size.

116

DISTRIBUTION AND HABITAT: Both these species are fairly widespread, and occur around most of the coast of Britain and all round Ireland. However, the worm pipefish has not been recorded from Britain's east coast and the straight-nosed pipefish has not been recorded from the northern half of Scotland. The worm pipefish lives in very shallow water in rocky areas amongst seaweeds and under stones, and is common on the shore. It is therefore more likely to be seen by snorkellors and shore enthusiasts than by divers. The straight-nosed pipefish rarely occurs actually on the shore, but lives mostly between about 5–25m deep. It is common amongst sea-grass and long-stranded seaweeds such as the bootlace weed (*Chorda filum*) and the thong weed (*Himanthalia elongata*). It can therefore be found in both rocky and sandy areas.

BIOLOGY: As in all pipefish, the male has responsibility for the care of the eggs. The female lays the eggs into a shallow groove on the male's belly, where they stick firmly, and egg-carrying males can be found throughout the summer from May to August. The eggs do not have as much protection as in the larger pipefish, and the young hatch and are released into the water whilst relatively undeveloped at about 9–10mm long. They live in the plankton for some weeks whilst completing their development. Young worm pipefish 3–4cm long can be found on the shore in September to October. With their small mouths, these pipefish are restricted in their diet, and feed mostly on planktonic crustaceans such as copepods.

BEHAVIOUR: The worm pipefish is a master of camouflage, and varies its colour to suit the seaweed amongst which it is hiding. This and its shape make it very difficult to spot. When it swims, it does so in a slow motion that resembles the swaying of seaweed.

SIMILAR SPECIES: None in British waters.

KEY IDENTIFICATION FEATURES:

1. Slender, smooth, worm-like body.

2. No fins apart from the dorsal.

3. Snout upturned (worm).

4. Snout straight (straight-nosed).

5. Very dark colour (worm).

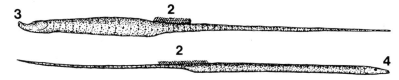

CONGER EEL *Conger conger*

DESCRIPTION: The conger eel is a familiar fish to most divers, with a largely-undeserved reputation for ferocity. Its scaleless snake-like body is long, smooth, and powerful, and ends in a pointed tail. There is a single, long dorsal fin which continues without interruption around the body, merging with the tail and anal fins. This fin starts only a short distance behind the head, almost overlapping the well-developed, pointed pectoral fins. This forward origin of the dorsal fin helps to distinguish young conger from common eels. Most divers only see the heads of conger eels peering out, with gaping jaws, from dark holes and corners. Most congers are a uniform brown on the back, contrasting with an off-white or pale brown belly. Those living in deeper water tend to be grey-brown to almost slate-blue.

SIZE: Congers commonly grow to a length of 2m, and some approach a length of 3m and a weight of 65kg. There is a record of a specimen weighing 114.5kg caught off Iceland.

DISTRIBUTION AND HABITAT: Congers occur all round Great Britain and Ireland, and are common in rocky areas where there are plenty of caves, holes and cracks in which they can hide. They are particularly common in shipwrecks, and will colonise any other man-made structures such as harbour walls, sea defences, and artificial reefs. Young congers are common on rocky shores, where they hide in deep, seaweed-filled rock pools. Adults range down to at least 1000m and spawn even deeper.

118

BIOLOGY: The conger eel has a similarly complex life history to that of the common eel, although it never enters fresh water. The complete story is not yet known. Congers do not spawn locally, but migrate out into the tropical Atlantic. There are thought to be several spawning grounds, that used by European populations being situated between Gibraltar and the Azores. Here it is thought that each female lays several million eggs in the open water at between 3000 to 4000m deep. The eggs develop into a larval fish that is so different from the adult, it was described as a separate species until the 1860's. The young fish (leptocephalus) is transparent, flattened and leaf-shaped. These larvae float to the surface and gradually drift back inshore over 1–2 years before they change into young eels. The enormous amount of energy expended on reproduction means that adults breed only once and then die. Observations on laboratory-kept fish have also shown that as the fish becomes sexually mature, the gut degenerates and the gonads increase hugely in size. The teeth also fall out and the bones lose calcium and become soft. In the wild this presumably does not happen until they near the breeding ground. The conger is a voracious feeder, only coming out of its lair to hunt at night.

BEHAVIOUR: Conger eel are enormously strong, and have a powerful bite, of which the diver should beware. However, they do not normally attack without provocation. During the day they can be found in their hidey-holes with only the head sticking out, and with care, can be closely approached and photographed. At night they range over the seabed in search of prey. Occasionally, a conger is reported as sharing his lair with another species, and divers have reported such an association with lobsters (Jim Greenfield, Marine Conservation Society Observation Scheme).

SIMILAR SPECIES: The common eel (*Anguilla*) and small conger might be confused, but several features can be used to separate them (see key identification features).

KEY IDENTIFICATION FEATURES:

1. Long, smooth, body; large jaws.

2. Continuous fin around body, the dorsal part starting near pectoral fin.

3. Pointed pectoral fins.

4. Jaws equal, or upper slightly longer than lower.

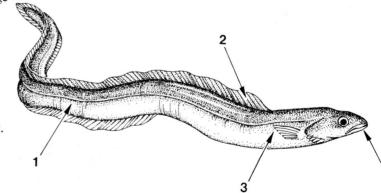

EEL   *Anguilla anguilla*

DESCRIPTION: The common eel is most often found in fresh water, but also lives on the shore and in coastal waters. Typically eel-shaped, it has a long, rounded, slippery body, and a small head, with the lower jaw longer than the upper. The single dorsal fin originates some way back on the body, and well clear of the pectoral fin. It is continuous around the body, with the tail and anal fins. The pectoral fins are rounded in outline. The colour is variable with the state of maturity. The normal feeding and growing phase is a muddy brown above and yellowish or golden on the sides and belly, and is called a yellow eel. It has rather a soft body and small eyes. The silver eel develops from the yellow eel as it starts to mature sexually, some time after about 7 years old. It is almost black on the back, and the sides and belly are silver. Other bodily changes include an increase in the size of the eyes and a hardening of the body.

SIZE: Females are much larger than males, normally reaching up to 1m long. Males are only about half this size. Exceptional individuals grow longer than a metre.

DISTRIBUTION AND HABITAT: Eels are widely distributed in fresh water throughout Great Britain and Ireland. They can also be found in shallow water all round the coast, especially near the shore and in estuaries. They are often found hiding in clumps of kelp and other seaweed and in seaweed-filled rock pools.

BIOLOGY: The life history of the eel is a complicated and fascinating affair, which is still incompletely documented. The yellow eel is the

120

normal feeding and growing phase found in rivers, lakes and estuaries. As these approach maturity at an age of anything from 4 to more than 10 years old, they change into silver eels. These migrate down the rivers to the sea in autumn. They do not remain in coastal waters for long, but set off on a remarkable migration of several thousand miles to the deep waters of the Atlantic Ocean, particularly the Sargasso Sea, which is thought to be the main breeding ground. During the journey it is assumed that the eggs mature and ripen, since ripe fish are not found inshore. Once at the breeding ground, the eggs are laid and fertilised in very deep water, and all the adults then die. The eggs hatch during March and April, and the tiny larvae rise to the surface to feed on plankton. The transparent, leaf-like larva is known as a leptocephalus, and was for a long time thought to be a separate species. The larvae gradually float back to Europe in the Gulf stream, taking about three years to reach shore. By this time they are about 7mm long, and quickly change into the familiar elvers that make their way up the rivers in countless millions each year. They resemble miniature, transparent adults. Once in a suitable habitat, they grow and develop into yellow eels. Yellow eels have a varied diet, depending on where they are living, including worms, molluscs, crustaceans, small fish, and insect larvae. Silver eels do not feed, living off fat reserves built up during the yellow eel phase. Eels form an important fishery, and large numbers of elvers, yellow eels and silver eels are caught during their migrations up and down river. They are also a favourite of birds such as waders and herons.

BEHAVIOUR: In fresh water, eels spend a lot of time hidden in the soft bottom mud. In estuaries and on coasts they often hide in holes with just the head showing, or in clumps of seaweed. They will sometimes "stand up" in a clump of seaweed for better concealment.

SIMILAR SPECIES: See under conger eel (*Conger conger*).

KEY IDENTIFICATION FEATURES:

1. Long, smooth, round body.

2. Continuous fin around body, the dorsal part starting well behind the pectoral fin.

3. Rounded pectoral fins.

4. Lower jaw longer than upper.

LING *Molva molva*

DESCRIPTION: The ling is a long, thin fish, with a single distinctive barbel on the chin. It has two soft dorsal fins, of which the first is short, and the second very long, extending nearly to the tail. The single anal fin is also long. In colour it is a mottled browny-green, usually lighter below. There is a dark patch at the rear of the first dorsal fin. The first dorsal fin and the anal fin are both outlined with white, and this usually shows up well under water. These two fins also have a dark blotch at the rear, but it is often not very clear. Young fish, which are often seen by divers, are usually a lighter brown with irregular pale marblings.

SIZE: Individuals seen by divers are usually a maximum of 1–1.5m long, but in deeper water specimens 2m long and up to 25kg are caught.

DISTRIBUTION AND HABITAT: Ling are found around the south-west peninsula of Britain, around Scotland and around the south and west coasts of Ireland. They are most often seen by divers on rocky, open coasts, deeper than about 20m, although they do occur as shallow as 10m. Typical habitats are under rocky overhangs, in rock fissures, and in wrecks. The majority of adults live in very deep water between 300–400m, and it is mostly the smaller, younger fish that live inshore, where the diver can see them.

BIOLOGY: Breeding occurs in spring and summer between March and July, in deep water between 100–300m. Spawning does not happen just anywhere, but in specific areas, particularly off southern Iceland, but also offshore on the 200m contour between Norway and the Bay of Biscay. The females lay enormous numbers of eggs – between 20–60 million – which float in the water and rise to the surface as they develop, hatching after about 10 days. The young fish tend to settle down in inshore waters moving offshore after 2 to 3 years. Not a great deal else is known about its biology. It feeds mainly on other fish, including Norway pout, cod, blue whiting, gurnard and flatfish, but also eats crustaceans and echinoderms. The latter two items may be more important to the smaller inshore fish. In Britain and the rest of Europe, there is a valuable commercial fishery for ling which are mostly caught on long lines. Much of the catch is salted and dried, but it is also eaten fresh and smoked.

BEHAVIOUR: Sightings by divers are not all that frequent, and little is known on any specific aspects of behaviour. The diver is most likely to see ling by searching under overhangs and in other hidey holes.

SIMILAR SPECIES: See rockling.

KEY IDENTIFICATION FEATURES:

1. Elongate body.

2. Long barbel on chin.

3. Two dorsal fins, first short, second long.

4. White edges to second dorsal fin and anal fin.

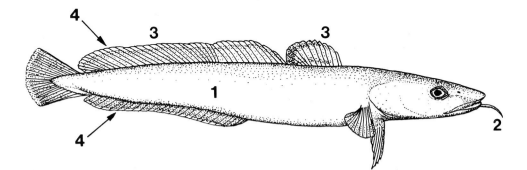

Shore rockling (left) and three-bearded rockling.

SHORE ROCKLING
Gaidropsaurus mediterraneus

THREE-BEARDED ROCKLING
Gaidropsaurus vulgaris

DESCRIPTION: Rocklings are long, slender relatives of the cod, with slippery and sometimes rather sinuous bodies. The shore rockling and the three-bearded rockling both have three barbels on the head – one on the chin and a pair near the tip of the snout. There are two dorsal fins, but in all rocklings the first one is very reduced, consisting of a fringe of very short rays with just a single long ray at the front. These may be difficult to see under water. The second dorsal fin and the single anal fin are both long and straight-edged. The two species can be told apart by the colour and the habitat (see below). The shore rockling is uniformly coloured brown, dark brown or reddish-brown, and has a lighter belly. The three-bearded rockling is salmon pink to brick red, or sometimes pale brown, and is characteristically marked with bold dark blotches. However, small fish (less than 10cm) may not have these blotches. If the fish can be closely examined, then the size of the mouth can help distinguish small fish. In the shore rockling it is small, and the corners of the jaws hardly extend past the eyes, whereas in the three-bearded rockling the mouth is large, and reaches well behind the eyes.

SIZE: The shore rockling reaches a length of at least 35cm, but most are between 15–25cm (hand length to forearm length). The three-bearded rockling is the largest of the rocklings, and can reach 53cm, but most reach only 40cm (length of hand plus forearm).

DISTRIBUTION AND HABITAT: The shore rockling is found only on the west and south coasts of Britain and all round Ireland. It has not

124

been recorded on the east coast of Britain. It is very rarely found in anything other than rocky areas, which may explain its absence from the east coast. It is common on the shore, and down to about 30m. It may occur deeper than this, but more diver records are needed to confirm this. The three-bearded rockling is less common, but more widely distributed, occurring all round Britain and Ireland. Thus a rockling with three barbels on the east coast is likely to be this species. It lives amongst rocks, but is equally happy on gravel and sand bottoms from just below the shore to at least 150m.

BIOLOGY: Both rocklings spawn offshore, the shore rockling in early summer and the three-bearded rockling in winter. The eggs and larval fish float in the plankton near the surface for several months before settling on the bottom when they are about 4–6cm long. The drifting juveniles are called "mackerel-midge" because mackerel feed on shoals of them. At this stage they are a clear green/blue on the back, with bright silvery sides and bellies, designed to provide camouflage in open water. Adults feed on crabs and other crustaceans, plus molluscs and small fish.

BEHAVIOUR: Rocklings are not always easy to see, as they tend to hide amongst rocks and seaweed, and with their slippery bodies they can hide in small crevices. If a diver can get close enough he may see the little rays of the first dorsal fin being rapidly vibrated. This appears to help in detecting food.

SIMILAR SPECIES: Superficially rockling resemble the ling (*Molva molva*), but the ling has only one barbel and has two distinct dorsal fins. The five-bearded rockling and the northern rockling have a very similar body shape and colouration to the shore rockling, but both of them have five barbels on the head. Another rockling, the four-bearded rockling (*Enchelyopus cimbrius*) lives mostly below 50m, but has been found as shallow as 20m. It has four barbels on the head.

KEY IDENTIFICATION FEATURES:

1. Long body.

2. First dorsal fin consists of short rays.

3. Three barbels.

4. Distinctly blotched (3-bearded).

5. Small mouth (shore), large mouth (3-bearded).

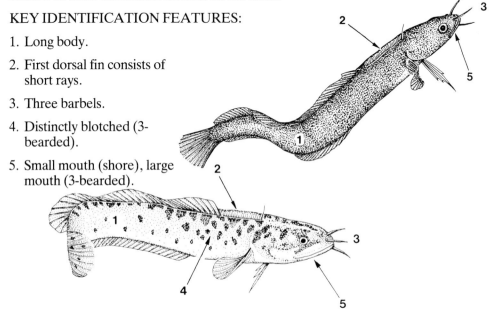

Five-bearded rockling.

FIVE-BEARDED ROCKLING
Ciliata mustela

NORTHERN ROCKLING
Ciliata septentrionalis

DESCRIPTION: These two rocklings are very similar in body shape and colour to the shore rockling. They have the long, slender body, and fringe-like first dorsal fin characteristic of this group (see shore rockling). The second dorsal fin and the single anal fin are both long. As its name suggests, the five-bearded rockling has five barbels – one on the chin, a pair just above the upper lip, and another pair just behind these near the tip of the snout. The northern rockling also has five barbels, and the two species are not easy to distinguish under water . In colour they are similar with a uniform brown, dark brown or reddish brown back and a paler underside. If a close view can be obtained then the size of the mouth will help identification. In the five-bearded rockling, this is small, and the corners of the jaws hardly extend back past the eyes, whereas in the northern rockling the mouth reaches well back past the eyes. The northern rockling also has a fringe of skin lobes along the top of the upper lip.

SIZE: The five-bearded rockling normally reaches 25cm (forearm length), but exceptionally can reach 45cm. The northern rockling normally reaches only 18cm (hand sized).

126

DISTRIBUTION AND HABITAT: Both species occur all round Great Britain and Ireland in rocky areas and on sand and mud bottoms. The five-bearded rockling is common, and lives in shallow water down to about 20m and on the shore. The northern rockling is much scarcer, and lives mostly in deeper water between 10–100m. It is sometimes common in rock pools on the north-eastern coast in summer. However, since the two species can be easily confused, the northern rockling may be commoner than the records suggest. Careful diver observations are needed to confirm this.

BIOLOGY: The five-bearded rockling spawns offshore in winter and early spring, and the northern rockling in spring (April–May), at least in southern Britain. As in other rocklings, the eggs float in the plankton and the young fish known as "mackerel-midge" (see shore rockling) drift in the surface waters for a few months before settling down on the seabed. The "mackerel-midge" are eaten by mackerel and other fish, and by seabirds, since they float near the surface.

BEHAVIOUR: On the shore the five-bearded rockling can be found hiding in depressions under boulders or in seaweed-filled rock pools. See also comments under the shore rockling.

SIMILAR SPECIES: The shore rockling has a very similar colouration and body shape to these two species, but it has only three head barbels. See also comments under shore rockling.

KEY IDENTIFICATION FEATURES:

1. Long body.

2. First dorsal fin consists of short rays.

3. Five barbels on head.

4. Small mouth (5-bearded); large mouth (northern).

5. Skin lobes along upper lip (northern).

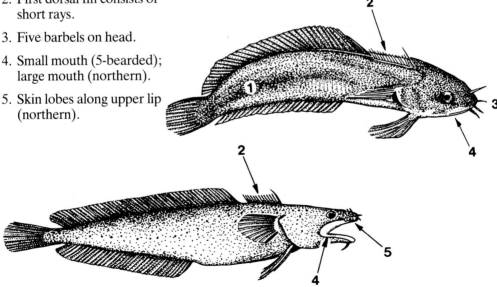

TADPOLE-FISH   *Raniceps raninus*

DESCRIPTION: The tadpole-fish is so called because it has a broad, flat head, and a stout, slippery body with a long relatively thin tail portion, rather like a tadpole. Like the rocklings it is a relative of the cod, and has the single chin barbel typical of most members of this group. There are two dorsal fins, the first very small and difficult to see as it consists of only three short rays. The second dorsal fin and the single anal fin are both long-based. The colour is almost black to very deep brown, but underneath it is greyish or whitish. The dark dorsal, tail and anal fins have a light edge, and the lips are also whitish.

SIZE: It can reach 30cm long, but is more usually 15–20cm (hand size).

128

DISTRIBUTION AND HABITAT: Although distributed all round the coasts of Great Britain and Ireland, the tadpole-fish is not very often seen by divers. It is not rare, but is easily overlooked, and there are relatively few records of it. It lives mostly amongst seaweeds in rocky areas just below the low tide mark, but also extends down to 100m, living amongst rocks and in areas of sand and mud.

BIOLOGY: It spawns in late summer to early autumn, generally below about 50–75m, where the temperature is fairly constant at between 10–12°C. The small eggs and larval fish float in the plankton, and the young settle down to life on the sea-bed in shallow coastal water when they have reached about 2cm long. Adults feed on shrimps, worms, small fish, echinoderms and other bottom-living animals.

BEHAVIOUR: This is a solitary fish that is never found in shoals, and spends much of its time on the bottom, hidden amongst seaweeds.

SIMILAR SPECIES: Superficially resembles some of the rocklings, especially in the shape of the head and the colour, but all rocklings have at least three barbels.

KEY IDENTIFICATION FEATURES:

1. More or less tadpole shape and colour.

2. First dorsal fin tiny.

3. Chin barbel.

4. Light edges to dorsal, anal and tail fins and light lips.

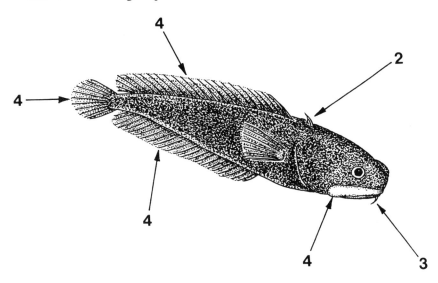

Three-spined stickleback (left) and fifteen-spined stickleback.

FIFTEEN-SPINED STICKLEBACK
Spinachia spinachia

THREE-SPINED STICKLEBACK
Gasterosteus aculeatus

DESCRIPTION: Two species of stickleback can be found around the coasts of Great Britain. The one most likely to be seen by divers is the 15-spined species which lives only in the sea. The common and well known 3-spined stickleback is equally at home in fresh and sea-water. Sticklebacks are small, torpedo-shaped fish, with a row of sharp spines along the back in front of the dorsal fin, from which they get their name. The 15-spined stickleback is a long, slim fish, with a very narrow tail stalk and a rounded tail fin. It has 15 spines on its back (occasionally 14 or 16), and a single small spine with one soft ray, in place of the pelvic fin. Its body appears rather stiff due to a series of protective bony plates running along both sides of the body. The 3-spined stickleback is stouter, has only 3 spines on its back, and has a long pelvic fin spine. It usually has a few bony plates along its sides. Both species are a greeny-brown colour, but in the sea the 3-spined species is often bluish with silvery sides. In the breeding season the males of the 3-spined species develop a bright red colour on the throat.

SIZE: The fifteen-spined stickleback can reach 20cm long, but is more usually 15cm (small hand size). The three-spined stickleback is usually only about 5cm long (little finger size) but can reach 10cm.

DISTRIBUTION AND HABITAT: Both sticklebacks are found all round Great Britain and Ireland in shallow water amongst seaweeds and seagrass. In England the 3-spined stickleback is found mostly in fresh water and in estuaries and tidal pools. In Scotland and further north it is common in coastal waters. The 15-spined species is found only in the sea down to about 10m depth. Its shape and colouration provide it with good camouflage, and it is not always easy to spot.

130

BIOLOGY: The breeding behaviour of the 3-spined stickleback is a complicated affair that has been well studied. Spawning occurs in spring and early summer when the male develops his bright red breeding colours. The male builds a nest on the bottom by building up a pile of seaweed, or other aquatic plants, and binding them together with a sticky substance produced by the kidneys. When the mound is complete, he burrows through it, thereby creating a hollow nest. He then entices several females successively through the nest, where each lays several hundred eggs. The male immediately follows each female through the nest to fertilise the eggs. The female's role is now finished, but the male remains to guard and oxygenate the eggs by fanning water over them. He is extremely aggressive at this time and will drive other fish out of his territory. The eggs hatch a few days to a few weeks later, depending on the temperature, and the male keeps the young near the nest for about a week, bringing them back in his mouth if they stray. After this time he starts to lose interest and they gradually disperse. The 15-spined stickleback also builds a nest in spring or summer, and this is always placed well clear of the bottom. A suitable seaweed is chosen, and its fronds are bound together with the sticky kidney secretion to form a fist-sized structure. Again it is the male that guards the 200 or so eggs laid by the female, and these hatch after about 20 days. Young sticklebacks of both species grow quickly, and are adults within their first year. They live for only 2 to 3 years. They feed mostly on small animals such as copepods, amphipods, worms and the spawn and fry of other fish. They are in turn eaten by larger fish and by birds fishing in the shallows and rock pools.

BEHAVIOUR: Sticklebacks can be quite closely watched by divers, since they tend to remain within a small area, especially the males in the breeding season.

SIMILAR SPECIES: The 15-spined stickleback is superficially similar in shape to some of the pipefish, and lives in a similar habitat. However, the spines on the back clearly identify it.

KEY IDENTIFICATION FEATURES:

1. Row of sharp spines along the back – the number denoting the species.

2. Pelvic fin is a single spine and one soft ray.

3. Bony plates along the flanks.

4. Very narrow tail stalk (15-spined).

Female cuckoo wrasse.

CUCKOO WRASSE
Labrus mixtus (= Labrus ossifagus)

DESCRIPTION: There is no mistaking this, one of the most colourful and entertaining of British fish. The cuckoo is a slim-line wrasse with a pointed head and snout, and has the usual wrasse characteristics of a single, long dorsal fin, and thick, fleshy lips. Females are a beautiful rose-pink to orange-red colour, and have three distinct black blotches interspersed with white on the back, under the soft rear portion of the dorsal fin. Males have dark blue heads, with brilliant blue lines and blotches that extend along the flanks. The rest of the body and the fins are bright orange to dull pink, and the fins also have blue markings. Sometimes fish intermediate in colour between the "female" and "male" can be seen, and this is explained below.

SIZE: Large males can reach a length of 35cm (forearm plus hand length). The females are generally smaller.

DISTRIBUTION AND HABITAT: Cuckoo wrasse can be found in rocky areas round most of the coasts of Britain and Ireland. However, they are not as common or ubiquitous as the ballan wrasse, and are most often seen in summer around deep, rocky reefs, and cliffs below about 10m. Some, at least, migrate offshore in winter into deeper warmer water extending down to at least 180m.

132

BIOLOGY: Males and females have such contrasting colour patterns that originally they were described as separate species. Like the ballan wrasse, cuckoos are born female, and then some of them change sex and colour, and become functional males. Thus you will never find small cuckoo wrasse with the blue colouration since this is not developed until the fish change sex between 7–13 years of age. Cuckoo wrasse are highly territorial, and spawn in pairs. Their fascinating courtship has so far only been fully observed in captivity. After excavating or selecting a hollow in the sea-bed for a nest, the male attracts females by an elaborate display. During this time his whole head may blanch to a pure white in a matter of seconds, the colour re-appearing just as quickly. Further courtship leads to spawning, and during the whole ritual, the nest-holding male will fiercely drive off other males. Males with white heads have been seen in the wild during early spring. To further complicate matters, it has now been found that a very few fish are born male but with the female colour. These "primary" males do not seem to take part in reproduction. Cuckoo wrasse are slow growing, and live for at least 17 years. They feed mainly on crustaceans, molluscs and worms, and can easily be caught on a rod and line.

BEHAVIOUR: Like the goldsinny wrasse, the cuckoo is a very inquisitive fish. The males in particular will often swim right up to a diver, and even peer into his face mask. This is especially so in areas often frequented by non-spearfishing divers, but even in remote areas, the diver is the one likely to be watched! In some areas such as the breakwater at Port Erin in the Isle of Man, the same fish, recognizable by a particular physical abnormality, has been seen in several consecutive summers.

SIMILAR SPECIES: None. Confusion is unlikely, even in small fish.

KEY IDENTIFICATION FEATURES:

1. Pointed head.

2. Females with 3 black blotches on back.

3. Males with blue head and lines.

BALLAN WRASSE   *Labrus bergylta*

DESCRIPTION: The ballan is the largest of the five species of wrasse commonly found around our coasts. It is a solid-looking fish, with a large head and thick fleshy lips. The single, long dorsal fin, has a sharply spiny front portion, and a soft–rayed, rear portion. It is very variable in colour, but most are basically a mottled green or brown, or occasionally reddish, with a paler underside and pale spots on the fins. The scales tend to have a dark edge and a paler centre, and in some fish this is greatly accentuated, giving a very spotty appearance. There is no colour difference between males and females, but large, old fish with a basically orange colour and white reticulations and spots have mostly proved to be males. Young fish in rock pools are mostly emerald green.

SIZE: The maximum size is about 60cm (an arm's length) but this is exceptional. A more usual adult size is 30–40cm.

DISTRIBUTION AND HABITAT: This familiar fish is very common on almost all the coasts of Britain and Ireland. However, since it prefers to remain close to rocks, it is rarely found in silty areas like the coastal waters

134

of East Anglia. It is at home on rocky reefs and in the kelp forest, where it can be seen swimming purposefully along, singly, or in small groups of three or four. The young are common in rock pools, where there is plenty of seaweed cover, and occasionally, larger fish become stranded there too. Adults range down to at least 30m, but are commonest above 20m or so.

BIOLOGY: The ballan has a very curious life history, but one which is not uncommon amongst members of the wrasse family. The eggs are laid in summer in a nest built of fine seaweed, and wedged into a rock crevice. They hatch after a few weeks and the small larval fish float away in the plankton, finally settling in shallow water. All these young fish are females. They grow very slowly, and are not mature until at least six years old. After several seasons spawning as females, some may change sex and become functional males, although there is no sign of this externally. The sex change usually occurs when the fish is quite old, but can occur as young as seven or eight years. The exact mechanism that causes some females but not others to change sex is not yet fully understood, but the result is considerably more females than males in any population of fish. Ballan wrasse live for a very long time, and fish of 25 years old are not unusual. They live mainly on shellfish, particularly mussels, and on crustaceans, including crabs and even barnacles. In addition to their normal teeth, there is a set of powerful crushing teeth in the throat, that enable the fish to tackle such tough fare. There have only been one or two observations of the nesting and mating behaviour of the ballan, and diver pictures and observations would be very useful.

BEHAVIOUR: The ballan has the interesting habit of "sleeping" at night, wedged firmly into a rock crevice, or hidden in strands of thick seaweed. They are very torpid at this time, and have even been picked up by divers before waking sufficiently to swim off hurriedly. They normally swim with a rowing motion, using their pectoral fins, and this is a very characteristic feature of wrasse in general.

SIMILAR SPECIES: Large ballan wrasse are easily recognised, since the other species are all much smaller, or are brilliantly coloured (cuckoo wrasse). Small ballan are sometimes confused with corkwing or rock cook, but both these have distinguishing marks (see appropriate Key Identification Features).

KEY IDENTIFICATION FEATURES:

1. Single, long dorsal fin.

2. Thick lips.

3. Large size.

GOLDSINNY   *Ctenolabrus rupestris*

DESCRIPTION: The goldsinny is a small, slim wrasse, easily recognised by its characteristic colouration and markings. As its name suggests, it is a beautiful golden to reddish-brown colour, often with a slightly striped appearance along the flanks, and with a whitish belly. It has a very distinctive black spot on the top edge of the tail stalk, and just a glimpse of the tail is often enough to identify this charming little fish. There is another black spot on the front of the single dorsal fin, but this can only be seen when the fin is held erect.

SIZE: The usual adult size is about 12cm long (palm size) but some reach 18cm or so.

DISTRIBUTION AND HABITAT: Although widely distributed, and found round almost all the coasts of Britain and Ireland, this little wrasse is only locally common. It is not often recorded on the English east coast, due to lack of suitable habitat. It lives mostly in rocky areas where there are plenty of crevices and cracks to hide in but is also found in seagrass beds. A favoured habitat in Scotland is on the boulder slopes that often

136

form the edges of sea lochs, where numerous hidey holes are formed by the jumble of rocks. Although they can be found in rock pools on the shore, goldsinny tend to prefer deeper water between about 10 to 50m. This is in contrast to the rock cook and corkwing wrasse that prefer to remain mostly within the seaweed zone.

BIOLOGY: As yet, relatively little is known about this wrasse, and hardly anything is known about its breeding habits. There is no difference in colour between males and females, and there are no indications that this wrasse changes sex as the ballan and cuckoo wrasse do. The goldsinny has a varied diet, but is particularly fond of amphipods (sand hoppers). It also eats small molluscs, worms, and occasional brittle-stars. It has small, forward-pointing teeth at the front of the jaws that also enable it to tear off encrusting animals such as bryozoans (sea-mats) from rocks and seaweeds, and to extricate titbits from the recesses of kelp holdfasts.

BEHAVIOUR: The goldsinny is an extremely entertaining fish, and is fascinating to watch, both under water or in an aquarium. It has a natural curiosity, and can be enticed out from its hiding place by a diver holding a shiny object such as a camera close-up frame. In well-dived areas, especially where there is no spear fishing, they can often be fed by hand, and will nibble at a diver's fingers – they have sharp teeth!

SIMILAR SPECIES: The corkwing is the only other common British wrasse with a tail spot, but this is situated centrally on the tail stalk, not on the top side. In the extreme south-west of Britain another small wrasse with a tail spot similar to the goldsinny is very rarely encountered. This is the scale-rayed wrasse (*Acantholabrus palloni*), which is larger and of a greeny-brown colour.

KEY IDENTIFICATION FEATURES:

1. Black spot on top side of
   tail stalk.

2. Golden colour.

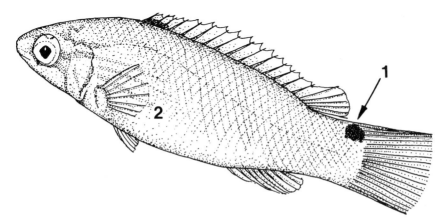

ROCK COOK or SMALL-MOUTHED WRASSE *Centrolabrus exoletus*

DESCRIPTION: One of the least well known of British wrasse, the rock cook is often mis-identified. However, it is easy to recognise once it has been encountered a few times. It is a small fish with a small mouth and head, but with the thick lips characteristic of this family. This, together with the single, long dorsal fin, and the habit of swimming with the pectoral fins, initially identifies it as one of the wrasse. The general body colour is a warm reddish-brown, grading into greenish-yellow on the flanks and white on the belly. Each scale has a blue-green tinge in the middle, which is accentuated in the males in the summer so that they become a beautiful bright violet blue. There are blue lines on the head in both sexes. Unlike the similarly-sized corkwing and goldsinny wrasse, it does not have a tail spot, but there is a broad, dark band across the tail fin. This is not always easy to see underwater.

SIZE: It usually grows to about 12cm long (large palm size), but some males reach 15cm.

138

DISTRIBUTION AND HABITAT: The rock cook can be found round much of Britain and Ireland, but is rather local in its distribution. It does not seem to occur on the east coast of England, or in the eastern half of the English Channel. It lives in shallow water amongst seaweed-covered rocks, and in seagrass beds down to about 25m depth. Unlike the ballan and corkwing wrasse, the young are rarely found in rock pools.

BIOLOGY: This is perhaps the least studied of all British wrasse, and there is little information on either its breeding or feeding habits. Males and females may be difficult to distinguish, but the males are gaudier, especially during the breeding season. There is no indication that this wrasse undergoes a sex-change as the ballan and cuckoo wrasse do. Females are in spawning condition by late spring. Observations are needed on the spawning behaviour especially in the wild. Nobody knows exactly what they eat, but they are often caught in lobster pots or fish traps, where they are probably feeding on small shrimps and other crustaceans attracted by the bait.

BEHAVIOUR: Although lacking the insatiable curiosity of the goldsinny and cuckoo wrasse, rock cook can nevertheless often be persuaded to approach divers and feed from their hands. This is especially the case in protected areas such as Loch Hine in southern Ireland, which is a National Nature Reserve. In captivity, they have been seen to act as cleaner fish, picking parasites off larger fish, and this probably also occurs in the wild.

SIMILAR SPECIES: The rock cook is most often confused with the corkwing, but the latter always has a tail spot, even if a rather faint one. Sometimes they are mistaken for small ballan wrasse, but the latter do not have the blue head lines of the rock cook.

KEY IDENTIFICATION FEATURES:

1. Dark bar across tail fin.

2. Blue lines on head.

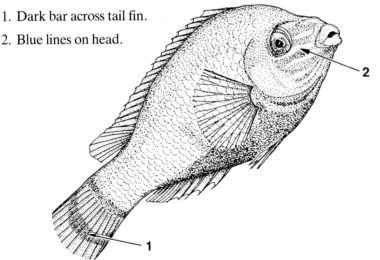

CORKWING WRASSE
Crenilabrus melops

DESCRIPTION: The corkwing is a typical, small, shallow-water wrasse. It is the most commonly seen of the three smaller British wrasse. With its thick lips, single long dorsal fin and habit of swimming with its pectoral fins, it is easily recognised as a wrasse. It has a deeper, stockier body than either of the similarly-sized rock cook and goldsinny wrasse. The basic colour is variable, and the sexes have different colour patterns, although these differences are more subtle than with the cuckoo wrasse. Commonly, they are a mottled brown, green or greeny-brown, occasionally reddish, with the centre of each scale being paler than the edges. In males, especially in the breeding season, the centres of the scales are bright green or blue, and there are numerous blue spots on the fins. Both sexes have lines on the head and gill covers – brown and pale blue in females, bright green or blue in males. All corkwing have a characteristic black spot in the middle of the tail stalk (the goldsinny has a spot at the *top* of the tail stalk). In very dark coloured fish, this may not be very clear. There is also a dark comma-shaped spot just behind the eye, most clearly seen in males.

SIZE: This small wrasse usually reaches about 15cm long (small hand size), but males may exceptionally reach 20–25cm.

DISTRIBUTION AND HABITAT: This is the commonest and most widespread of the smaller wrasse, and is found all round Britain and Ireland. It lives mostly in shallow water, but extends down to 30m or so. Divers will most often meet it amongst seaweed-covered rocks a little way below low-tide mark. Both young and adults can also be found in deep

140

seaweed-filled rock pools on the shore. During winter they tend to move off the shore to avoid extremes of temperature. Like the rock cook, corkwing can often also be found in seagrass beds.

BIOLOGY: The life history of this little wrasse has been well studied, and its preference for shallow water makes it easy for divers to study. Diver observations, particularly by Dr Geoff Potts in Plymouth, have shown that in the spring the males build an elaborate nest out of seaweed, siting it in a rock crevice. Each nest is aggressively guarded by its owner, who chases off all other males. Ripe females however, are enticed to the nest by an elaborate courtship display. The male recognises a receptive female from her colour, distended, egg-filled abdomen, and enlarged, blue-black egg-laying papilla near the anal fin. After the female has laid her eggs in the nest, the male fertilises them and covers them over with seaweed. He may then entice another female in. As well as guarding the eggs, he also oxygenates them by fanning water over them with his tail. After hatching, the larval fish disperse and float freely in the plankton. They drift inshore around late summer and autumn, and this is when most young can be found in the rock pools. There is no evidence to suggest a sex change in this wrasse, but it does have one unusual characteristic. In each population there appear to be a number of counterfeit or satellite males, which look exactly like females, but are functional young males. They may attempt to trick nest-building males into allowing them access to the nest, where instead of laying eggs, they try to fertilise any eggs already present. Corkwing feed mainly on small crustaceans, worms and molluscs, which they search out from the seaweed and undergrowth on the rocks.

BEHAVIOUR: Unlike the goldsinny and the cuckoo wrasse, the corkwing does not seem to have much natural curiosity. Unless frightened, it will normally totally ignore divers, and swim off on its own business with rapid beats of its pectoral fins. Like the rock cook, the corkwing has been observed in captivity to act as a cleaner fish, picking parasites off larger fish.

SIMILAR SPECIES: The corkwing is most commonly confused with young ballan or rock cook, but neither of these has a tail spot. Baillon's wrasse (*Crenilabrus bailloni*) has a tail spot in a similar position, but is a very rare visitor, and has only been recorded from the channel and from the west coast of Ireland a few times.

KEY IDENTIFICATION FEATURES:

1. Black spot in *middle* of tail stalk.

2. Comma-shaped spot behind eye.

3. Lines on head and gill covers.

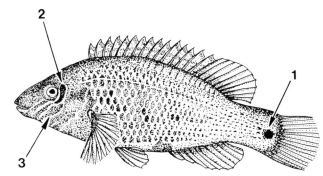

BLACK SEA-BREAM or OLD WIFE
Spondyliosoma cantharus

DESCRIPTION: The sea-bream could be described as typically fish-shaped. Oval in outline, it has a single long dorsal and anal fin and a large, forked tail. The mouth is small, the corner only just reaching back as far as the eye, and the jaws are equal in length. The profile of the head is smoothly convex in the young, but changes to concave in mature males, which also have a slightly "humped" shoulder. A diver sees the adults as large, completely silvery fish, although some have 6 to 9 dusky, vertical bars on the sides. Nesting males are often almost black in colour, hence the common name, and spawning males also develop an iridescent blue-grey band between the eyes. The juveniles are more colourful, and usually have numerous broken yellowish stripes along the sides, spotted fins, and a dark edge to the tail which often persists into adult life.

142

SIZE: The usual size is up to 35 or 40cm (the length of a hand and forearm), but some individuals reach 50cm or more.

DISTRIBUTION AND HABITAT: The black sea-bream occurs all round Britain and Ireland, but sightings by divers are relatively scarce. It is near the northern limit of its distribution around Britain, and although it breeds in the English Channel, is probably only a summer visitor to the rest of the country. Most sightings by divers have been from around wrecks and rocks on the south coast. Further south in the Mediterranean, it lives over sand and seagrass meadows, and it may well frequent similar habitats in Britain.

BIOLOGY: In the English Channel, the fish spawns in April and May. Unlike most other bream, it lays its eggs in a nest – a depression in the sand which the male excavates with his tail. The eggs are sticky, and so remain in the bottom of the nest. The male guards the nest until the young hatch, and they remain near home for several weeks before venturing further afield. In common with many other members of their family (Sparidae), the black sea-bream is a hermaphrodite, and undergoes a change in sex during its life. Bream are regularly caught by anglers but are not common enough to be commercially exploited.

BEHAVIOUR: Large adults are not easy to approach under water, and will dart off as soon as they see a diver – probably the reason they are not seen more often. Divers have seen them swimming in lines of several fish, led by the largest fish, and juveniles have been seen feeding over sediment with red mullet (observation by Mark Deeble). The red mullet may stir up food items which the bream then snap up.

SIMILAR SPECIES: Other large, silvery fish commonly encountered all have 2 or more dorsal fins. Eight other sea-bream occur in British waters, but most are uncommon to very rare, with their centre of distribution down in the Mediterranean. The red sea-bream occurs fairly regularly, but is distinguished by its rosy colour and blackish spot on the flank.

KEY IDENTIFICATION FEATURES:

1. Large, silvery fish (adults).

2. Single, long dorsal fin.

3. Small mouth and lips.

4. Blue-black rim on tail,
especially in young fish.

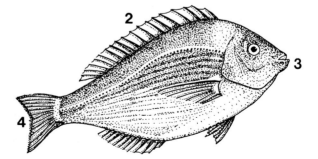

TWO-SPOTTED GOBY
Gobiusculus flavescens

DESCRIPTION: As its name implies, this small, slender goby is most easily recognised from its characteristic spots, but its habitat and behaviour are also distinct from those of other commonly-encountered gobies. At the base of the tail fin in both males and females is a large black spot with a pale edge. In addition, males have another similar spot on the sides, beneath the first dorsal fin. The background colour is a reddish brown with darker reticulations and pale saddle markings along the back. Along the mid-line of the sides is a series of alternate dark and pale bluish marks, which are accentuated in the breeding season, making the males in particular very colourful. Another characteristic feature, but one of little use to the diver, is that the first dorsal fin has 7 rays as distinct from the more usual 6 in other gobies.

SIZE: Up to 6cm (finger-sized).

144

DISTRIBUTION AND HABITAT: The two-spotted goby can be found all round the coasts of Britain and Ireland. The diver will encounter it in shallow water down to about 15m, hovering in small groups above seaweed-covered rocks, and up among the stipes and fronds of the kelp forest. It also frequents seagrass beds and deep rock pools where wracks and other large brown seaweeds grow. The two-spotted goby is unusual amongst gobies in spending most of its life in the water column rather than living down on the seabed.

BIOLOGY: The female lays her eggs from May to July in the hollow holdfasts of brown seaweeds, attaching them firmly by one end. The male then guards the eggs until they hatch, and so will be found at this time near to the seabed. Not surprisingly considering the semi-pelagic life style, the two-spotted goby feeds on floating (planktonic) animals such as copepods, and crustacean and molluscan larvae, which it catches by suddenly darting forward.

BEHAVIOUR: Small shoals can be seen characteristically hovering quietly above and amongst seaweeds, waiting to snap up food items. Individuals will often remain still enough to be photographed even with a close-up frame on the camera, provided the diver is gentle enough in his movements.

SIMILAR SPECIES: The markings and behaviour of this species distinguish it from all other commonly-encountered gobies.

KEY IDENTIFICATION FEATURES:

1. Conspicuous black, pale-rimmed spot at base of tail fin.

2. In males a similar spot on the sides under the dorsal fin.

3. Hovers in small shoals above seaweeds.

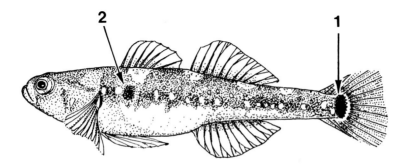

DORY or JOHN DORY   *Zeus faber*

DESCRIPTION: The dory is one of the most distinctive of all British fish. Resembling a dinner plate with fins, it has a rounded but very thin body, and a large head with a heavy, protrusible mouth. The single dorsal and anal fins have a sharp, spiny front portion, and the dorsal spines extend into long, elegant filaments. Running round the edge of the body is a double series of sharp spiny scales. The colour is generally a dark grey or yellowish brown with lighter yellow "camouflage" markings, and a silver or white belly. There is a large black blotch circled with yellow in the middle of each side – according to legend, the mark of St. Peter's thumb, made when he took a piece of money from the fish's mouth.

SIZE: The usual size is up to 40cm (about hand and forearm length).
Females have occasionally been known to reach 66cm.

DISTRIBUTION AND HABITAT: Although it can be found all
round Britain and Ireland, the dory is comparatively rare in the North Sea,
and is most often seen off Britain's south and south-west coasts. It is
generally found close inshore between about 10 and 50m, although it does
range down to 200m. Divers usually see single specimens hovering
between strands of seaweeds in both rocky and sandy areas. Long strands
of bootlace weed and seagrass provide good cover for this stealthy hunter.

BIOLOGY: Generally a solitary fish, the dory can sometimes be found
in small groups, mainly of young fish. It spawns in summer, but Britain is
at the northern end of its range, and it is doubtful if it breeds further north
than the western English Channel, or possibly the southern Irish Sea.
Older fish stay near the spawning grounds, and so it is usually the younger
fish which travel further afield that are seen by divers. The dory is an
expert hunter, stalking its prey – mostly small fish – by a stealthy, head-on
approach. In this attitude, the thin body makes it almost invisible, allowing
it to get within striking distance, when the protrusible jaws are shot out to
engulf the prey. In spite of its rather grotesque apperance, the dory makes
good eating, and is fished for on a small scale, being trawled up from
sandy areas.

BEHAVIOUR: The dory is not a good swimmer, but like the infamous
fresh water pike, it is very good at underwater manoeuvres, spending
much of its time hovering quietly in the water column. The thin body
allows it a good view backwards, and it will often present its tail to a
watching diver, ready to dart off. It can swim quite fast, but only for short
distances, and with patience it can be stalked and photographed. Divers
have even been able to stroke these fish under water, particularly at night.

SIMILAR SPECIES: Confusion with other species is unlikely. In
British waters, its closest relative is the boar fish (*Capros aper*), which is
not found above 100m or so.

KEY IDENTIFICATION FEATURES:

1. Unmistakable shape.

2. Large, yellow-rimmed,
   black spot on each side.

3. Hovers in the water.

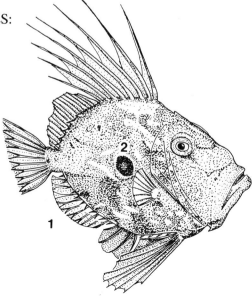

COD   *Gadus morhua*

DESCRIPTION: The cod will be a familiar fish to most people since it forms one of Britain's most important commercial fisheries. It is a powerful, heavily built fish with a large head and a single long chin barbel. The upper jaw is longer than the lower jaw and overhangs it. The 3 dorsal and 2 anal fins have rounded outlines and the tail fin is square-cut or slightly rounded. One of the cod's most distinctive characteristics is the curved lateral line which is conspicuously white and usually very obvious to a diver even in murky water. It is not so obvious in very young fish. The colour is variable according to the habitat. Many are a mottled sandy brown, since they are often found over sandy bottoms. The individual cod seen by divers around wrecks and rocks are usually a dull green, mottled with brown. "Red" cod are also sometimes found and young fish (5-10cm) are frequently an orange-brown with a distinctly chequered pattern. The belly is generally a dirty white.

SIZE: An average sized adult cod is usually about 120cm long, weighing 11kg or so. Larger fish up to 45kg or so are much rarer nowadays, and there is a historical record from the 17th century of a 90kg cod. A specimen caught in the Barents Sea was 169cm long and 24 years old. Age and growth estimates give lengths of about 18cm by 1 year, 36cm by 2 years and 53 cm by 3 years.

DISTRIBUTION AND HABITAT: The cod has a wide distribution and is found in all the waters around Britain and Ireland. It lives in a variety of habitats and has an extensive depth range from just below the shore to 60m or so. It is mostly the younger, smaller fish that live close inshore and so these are the most likely to be seen by divers. Larger

148

individuals are sometimes seen by divers around wrecks or large rocks, and swimming under schools of bib. They are much more abundant in the cooler waters off Scotland than in the south, but around Great Britain they tend to migrate southwards in winter to feed, and so become more common in the Channel and off East Anglia at this time. In early spring they migrate northwards again towards the cooler, deeper spawning grounds. Cod are also more likely to be in shallow water in the winter – perhaps the reason they are not often seen by divers.

BIOLOGY: Cod are prolific breeders, and in one spawning a good sized adult female lays between 3 to 6 million eggs. The eggs are shed into the sea between February and April at a depth of about 200m in one of many well defined spawning grounds. In the North Sea these grounds may be between 20m and 100m. The eggs and larvae rise towards the surface and drift in the ocean currents often forming great swarms. The few that survive uneaten gradually drift into shallower water and take up a bottom-living existence at a length of a few centimetres, by the autumn of their first year. Young fish feed mostly on copepods, but older fish eat a wide variety of seabed animals, including crabs, lobsters, prawns, worms, brittle-stars, sea urchins and shellfish (which are eaten whole). They will also catch other fish such as herrings, sprats, flatfish, sand eels and their own young. In turn they are eaten by seals, dolphins and halibut, but their greatest predator is man.

BEHAVIOUR: Divers can sometimes see cod "grazing" the seabed, searching out crabs and other animals hiding in the undergrowth. At this time it is possible to stalk them fairly closely, but they are shy, and will dash off at the click or flash of a camera. On a night dive or in fairly deep water, a diver might hear cod communicating by a series of loud, low grunts. These are produced with the help of the muscles of the swim-bladder and are mostly used in courtship. The courtship involves the male erecting his fins and twisting and turning in front of the female to attract her attention. This has only been observed in aquaria.

SIMILAR SPECIES: Although the young of several species may be confused with those of the cod, the white lateral line in adults should make them unmistakable. The most likely confusion is with the poor cod but these only grow to about 20cm

KEY IDENTIFICATION FEATURES

1. Three dorsal and 2 anal fins.

2. Light coloured lateral line.

3. Overhanging upper jaw.

4. Long chin barbel.

5. Mottled colour.

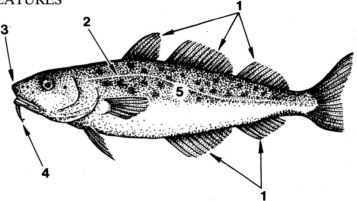

HADDOCK *Melanogrammus aeglefinus*

DESCRIPTION: The haddock is a graceful-looking fish, with a relatively small head and large eyes. The 3 dorsal and 2 anal fins are each distinctly separate, with spaces between, and the first dorsal fin is a characteristic, tall, triangular shape. As in the cod and bib, the upper jaw is longer than the lower one, but it has only a very short chin barbel. Perhaps the most characteristic feature, easily seen by a diver, is the large black mark, like a thumbprint, just behind the pectoral fin and below the distinctive black lateral line. In young fish this mark is particularly clear, and may be ringed with white. The background colour is a dark greeny-brown or purple brown on the back, shading to dark greyish silver on the sides and to white on the belly.

SIZE: The usual commercial length is between 38 to 64cm (½ to 1 arm length) but it may reach 76cm. The largest fish on record was 112cm long and weighed nearly 17kg.

DISTRIBUTION AND HABITAT: Haddock can be found all round Great Britain and Ireland, but are not often seen by divers, since they live

150

mostly in depths below 40m and down to 300m. However, they will feed at depths of as little as 20m, and so come within the diver's range. They spend most of the time feeding close to the seabed, but shoals are occasionally found in mid-water.

BIOLOGY: Spawning takes place in spring between February to June, and follows a courtship that involves grunting sounds as well as visual displays. It mostly occurs in deep water, and is unlikely to be observed by scuba divers. Between 10,000 and 1 million eggs are laid by each female, the large numbers compensating for the high losses that occur as the buoyant eggs drift to the surface and float in the ocean currents. The larvae and fry remain in the plankton until the autumn of their first year, by which time they are 5cm or so long. They then move down to the seabed to join the adults. Whilst in the plankton, some young fish take up residence under the bell of large jellyfish, such as the lion's mane jellyfish (*Cyanea* sp.) and *Rhisostoma pulmo* (see also whiting). Whilst in the plankton, the young fish feed mainly on copepods, but adults feed almost entirely on bottom-living animals such as worms, brittlestars and molluscs. Sand eels and capelin are sometimes eaten in large numbers, and also eggs from the herrings spawning grounds. In some years survival rates of young fish may be particularly good, and haddock will be abundant in areas where they might normally be scarce. Numbers have declined because of man's fishing activities, but it is still possible to see huge shoals of young fish in shallow water. The haddock is almost as important commercially as the cod, and something over 300,000 tons are caught annually by British fishing boats.

BEHAVIOUR: Haddock are very wary fish – another reason why they are not often seen by divers. Their wariness probably results from their being frightened by the noise of a diver's breathing. They appear to be very sensitive to noise, which is not surprising, since they use sound as a means of communication, particularly during courtship. Only a quiet and patient diver will get close enough to photograph these fish, and it is usually necessary to lure the fish closer with some food, such as broken-up mussels.

SIMILAR SPECIES: Confusion is unlikely as long as the black thumbprint on the fish's side can be seen.

KEY IDENTIFICATION FEATURES:

1. Three dorsal and two anal fins.

2. Pointed, triangular first dorsal fin.

3. Black thumbprint mark on sides.

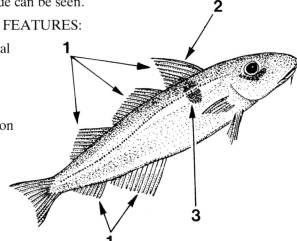

WHITING

Merlangius merlangus
(= Gadus merlangus)

DESCRIPTION: The whiting is a relatively slender member of the cod family, with a narrow and somewhat pointed head. As in the cod and poor cod, the upper jaw is longer than the lower jaw, but it has no chin barbel (the young have a minute barbel). The three dorsal and two anal fins are joined at their bases, and the first anal fin is long. The tail fin is square cut or rounded. It is rather a neutral colour, with a sandy to bluey green back and conspicuously silvery white sides and belly. There is a small black mark at the base of the pectoral fin. The diver will also notice that the edges of the anal fins have a distinct white border – a feature that does not show in dead fish.

SIZE: The usual size is around 30–40cm (forearm length), but it occasionally reaches 70cm.

152

DISTRIBUTION AND HABITAT: Whiting are very common all round Britain and Ireland, and are most abundant between 25 to 100m. For all their abundance, they are not often seen by divers, perhaps because most of the larger ones live over sand and mud, and in depths greater than normal diving limits. However, the fish's neutral colours blend in very well with the background, and this may be another reason. Around inshore wrecks and rocks it is mostly the smaller, younger fish that the diver sees.

BIOLOGY: Whiting spawn in open water between January to July, but around Britain, mostly in the early spring. The spawning time depends on the water temperature, and 5–10°C seems to be optimal. Females can produce up to 300,000 eggs over a period of up to 8 weeks. After hatching, the young fish drift in the plankton for as long as a year, and during this time, young fish of 3cm or so are often found sheltering amongst the tentacles of large jellyfish such as *Cyanea lamarkii* and *Chrysaora isocoles*. When danger threatens, the young fish swim up inside the bell of the jellyfish, but it is not certain how the jellyfish benefits from the relationship, or exactly why it does not sting the young whiting. As they grow, the young whiting move down towards the seabed, where they feed on shrimps and other crustaceans. Later, the diet is widened to include small fish such as sand eels, sprat and the young of herring and gadoids. A normal life span is 5–7 years, although some individuals may reach 12–13 years. Man is the greatest predator of the whiting, which is a very important commercial food fish. It is also widely eaten by other larger fish and by sea birds, since it frequently comes near the surface.

BEHAVIOUR: The whiting appears to feed most actively at dawn and dusk – which may be the best time for the diver to see them.

SIMILAR SPECIES: All the other gadoid fish commonly encountered by divers and described in this book have a chin barbel, except for the pollack and saithe, with which confusion is unlikely.

KEY IDENTIFICATION FEATURES:

1. No chin barbel.

2. White edge to anal fins.

3. Small black spot at base of pectoral fin (also in poor cod and bib).

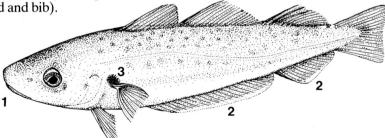

POOR COD   *Trisopterus minutus*

DESCRIPTION: Poor cod should perhaps be called poor bib, because they resemble small, unstriped bib, and belong to the same genus (*Trisopterus*). Like the bib, the upper jaw is longer than the lower jaw, and so overhangs it, and there is a long chin barbel. The 3 dorsal and 2 anal fins are set close together, with no gap between the bases. However, the poor cod is a slimmer, more delicate fish than the bib, and the overall impression in the water is of a uniformly shiny, coppery-coloured fish. The back is a yellowish brown to bronze red, with lighter coppery flanks and a silvery grey belly. It is never striped like the bib or mottled like the cod. There is a small black spot at the base of the pectoral fin (also in bib and whiting).

SIZE: Usually about 15–20cm (hand-sized) but occasionally reaches 26cm.

DISTRIBUTION AND HABITAT: The poor cod is abundant all round the coasts of Britain and Ireland in depths of 25–300m. It does go into shallow water, but not as commonly as the bib. It forms schools

154

close to the bottom or in mid-water in the same sorts of places as the bib. The diver will most commonly see them in small schools around wrecks or other artificial structures and off most rocky coasts. Where the seabed consists of a slope or jumble of large boulders, such as is common in many of the Scottish sea lochs, small groups of poor cod can usually be found sheltering in the cave-like spaces between the rocks. They can also be seen searching for food just above the seabed in sediment areas such as the bottoms of sea lochs.

BIOLOGY: Like the bib, the poor cod spawns in deep water – usually between about 50–100m at temperatures above 8°C. It spawns in winter in the south, but around Britain, especially in the north, it must wait until spring (March–April) when the water has warmed up. It has a life span of up to 6 years. Poor cod are mainly bottom-feeders, taking molluscs and crustaceans, but the older, larger individuals will also take fish. It in turn forms an important part of the diet of larger fish, such as cod and dolphins. Large numbers are taken by man, but these are only used for processing as fish meal.

BEHAVIOUR: Poor cod are not as friendly as bib, but are not particularly wary of divers. When they are sheltering between rocks they can often be enticed out by the glint of a camera or other shiny object.

SIMILAR SPECIES: The most likely confusion is with small bib, especially if the bib's stripes do not show clearly. Young cod usually have a mottled appearance, and young whiting, pollack and saithe have no (or very small) chin barbels.

KEY IDENTIFICATION FEATURES:

1. Three dorsal and two anal fins.

2. Long chin barbel.

3. Uniform bronze colour.

4. Relatively big eyes.

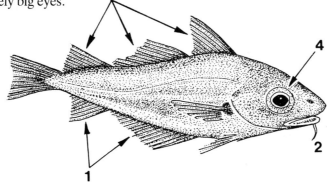

BIB, POUTING, POUT or
WHITING POUT *Trisopterus luscus*

DESCRIPTION: The bib is relatively easy to distinguish from other similar species, and the diver should be able to recognise this species from the colour alone. It is basically a beautiful, dark coppery brown, with 3 or 4 lighter bands running vertically down the body. The overall effect is thus of wide, dark bands, alternating with narrow pale bands. However, in older fish the pale bands tend to disappear and the large bib may be completely dark brown. There is also a conspicuous black dot at the base of the pectoral fin. It has a much deeper body than most of its relatives, and has its 3 dorsal and 2 anal fins set close together, so that there are no real gaps between them. The first dorsal fin is high and distinctly pointed. Like the cod, it has a single, long chin barbel, and the upper jaw is longer than the lower jaw and overhangs it.

SIZE: The usual adult size is between about 20 to 30cm (1 to 2 hand lengths). Larger fish up to 45cm are not uncommon, and divers report seeing very large fish up to about 60cm hiding in the dim recesses of wrecks.

DISTRIBUTION AND HABITAT: Bib are common all round the British Isles and Ireland. Large shoals of several hundred fish can be found around rocky reefs, and they are particularly attracted to wrecks, where divers most commonly encounter them. The preferred habitat is of mixed rock and sand rather than entirely rocky areas. Young fish are common in shallow water in sandy areas in as little as 3m of water. Older, larger fish prefer deeper water, and extend down to about 300m. At wreck sites, any large bib will be found skulking in dark hiding holes within the wreck, whilst the smaller fish swim freely around the outside.

BIOLOGY: Most of the fish spawn between March and April at depths of 50–70m, but some spawn in shallower water and as late as August. The young fish mature when they are a year old, and the normal life span is 6–8 years. Bib feed mainly on crustaceans, especially shrimps, and on molluscs, and older individuals will catch small squid and fish. Bib are not of great commercial importance to man because they are relatively small in size, and their flesh is soft and easily spoilt. Local fisheries process them into fish meal. Divers have noticed that in some areas a few of the fish in each shoal have a white, fungus-like growth around their mouths, and tend to swim around with their mouths open (observation by Kendall McDonald in *Fish Watching and Photography*, 1972). It would be interesting to have further observations on this to see how widespread it is, and if it is connected in any way with local pollution.

BEHAVIOUR: One of the first things a diver will notice about bib is that they are not at all shy. They make excellent photographic subjects, and the problem may well be to keep them far enough away from you! They are constantly on the look-out for potential food items disturbed by the diver. They appear to use their long, flexible pelvic fins as well as the chin barbel in their search for food. Older, larger fish are less adventurous, and tend to remain in their hiding places.

SIMILAR SPECIES: The most likely confusion is of small specimens with poor cod (*Trisopterus minutus*). The plain colouration of the poor cod and its much narrower body should distinguish it, but occasionally the banding in the bib is not obvious. The haddock (*Melanogrammus aeglefinus*) also has a pointed first dorsal fin, but the colouration is different, and the chin barbel is very short.

KEY IDENTIFICATION FEATURES:

1. Three dorsal and two anal fins.

2. Deep body.

3. Pointed first dorsal fin.

4. Long chin barbel.

5. Vertical bands on body.

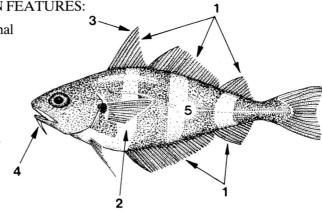

Pollack (left) and saithe.

POLLACK or LYTHE
Pollachius pollachius

SAITHE, COALFISH or COLEY
Pollachius virens

DESCRIPTION: Well-known to divers and to fishermen, the pollack and saithe are similar in shape and colour. Both are typical members of the cod family, with 3 dorsal and 2 anal fins, and relatively large eyes. A diver will usually first notice these beautiful fish when a glint of silver catches his eye. Their streamlined bodies are predominantly a silvery-white on the sides and belly, but a dark green to brownish green on the back. Older fish may be predominantly dark. Pollack and saithe can be distinguished by looking at the mouth and the lateral line. The pollack has a jutting lower jaw, clearly protruding beyond the upper, whereas in the saithe the jaws are more or less equal. The pollack's dark lateral line is sharply curved over the pectoral fin before straightening out again along the mid-line. In the saithe, the lateral line is straight and light coloured. Juveniles are more difficult to distinguish, and tend to be an overall greeney colour. Small gadoids (codfish) in general are not easy to distinguish.

SIZE: Both species can grow into very large fish over 1m long and weighing up to 14kg. An average-sized pollack is about 50cm (an arm's length) and an average saithe around 70–80cm.

DISTRIBUTION AND HABITAT: Pollack and saithe are common all round the British Isles and Ireland. Divers will most often see them in small schools around rocks and wrecks, to which they seem to be

158

attracted, and also swimming quietly above the kelp forest. Large, solitary individuals may lurk inside gullies or wrecks, but most remain out in the open. Young of both species are common close inshore amongst rocks and weeds, where their dark colouration renders them inconspicuous. Young pollack are also frequent over sandy beaches and in estuaries. The saithe is relatively more common than the pollack in the north, and first-year saithe are very common in Scottish rock pools. Both species range from the shore down to about 250m, and it is the large schools in mid-water that are commercially fished.

BIOLOGY: Spawning in both species occurs between January to April in deep water, between about 100–200m, with the pollack preferring the shallower end of the range. The eggs and larvae float in the plankton and drift towards shallower inshore waters – the preferred habitat of the young fish, which feed mainly on crustaceans. Adults feed mainly on fish, especially sand eels, herring, capelin and other open-water fish, mostly members of the cod and herring families. Divers may see pollack hanging head up at an angle in the water, sheltering in the lee of a rock or wreck, and waiting for the tide to bring some food their way. They swim up, snap up the food and sink rapidly down again. There are commercial fisheries for both the pollack and the saithe, but it is only the saithe that is of any real importance, with about 250,000 tons landed annually in European waters. They are good sporting fish, and are taken by anglers.

BEHAVIOUR: The schools of pollack and saithe so often seen quietly hanging around a wreck or above the kelp forest, are not particularly wary of divers, and with patience it is possible to get into the middle of a shoal. However, they react in a panic-stricken manner to the flash of a camera. Detailed studies have been made by divers of a school of saithe inhabiting a rocky reef in N.W. Scotland (article by Wyche in *Progress in Underwater Science*, 1984). Here the saithe appeared to use the reef as a home base during the day, patrolling in a school around the perimeter. At night they dispersed over the adjacent sand to feed.

SIMILAR SPECIES: The silvery colour, shape and behaviour of these two species should allow easy recognition.

KEY IDENTIFICATION FEATURES:

1. Three dorsal and two anal fins.

2. Silvery flanks and dark back.

3. Pollack: lower jaw juts out. Saithe: equal jaws.

4. Pollack: curved dark lateral line. Saithe: straight, light lateral line.

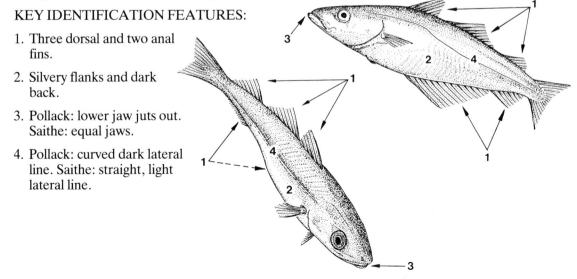

Section III. Open water and schooling fish

SOME FISH spend most or all of their time swimming in open water, and are not associated to any large degree with any particular type of sea-bed. Animals with this type of life style are called "pelagic", and include not only fish but squid, sea-birds, whales and dolphins as well. The majority of pelagic fish live and feed in large schools or shoals, and many make long migrations to breeding and feeding grounds.

Included here in this group are the herring and herring-like fish such as sprat and anchovy; mackerel and mackerel-like fish such as tuna and horse mackerel (scads); and the basking shark. Also included are the bass and mullet, since these are active schooling fish. However, these two species might better be described as semi-pelagic or semi-open water species, since although they move and feed in open water, they are consistently found in the immediate vicinity of rocky reefs (bass) and seaweed-covered sediments (mullet). In fact there are many species that fill this middle ground between truly open water species and those bound to a particular sea-bed type.

Open-water fish, especially small species such as sprat, cannot escape from predators by hiding amongst rocks or burying themselves in the sand. This is one of the reasons why so many of them live in the large shoals that are such a beautiful sight as they move and change direction in perfect unison. A predator hunting by sight finds it difficult to single out a particular target, becomes confused and will often miss entirely as it lunges into a shoal of fish. Most open-water fish are also protected by their colouration, which tends to be green or blue on the back and silvery white on the belly. This provides them with excellent camouflage, since to a predator looking down from above, the water appears greenish or bluish; and to one looking up from below, reflections from the surface make the water appear silvery.

Truly open-water fish feed mainly on floating (planktonic) animals, and on other smaller schooling fish. Even the great basking shark feeds entirely on plankton. Partially open-water species such as the mullet may feed both at the surface and on the sea-bed.

BASKING SHARK *Cetorhinus maximus*

DESCRIPTION: Most sightings of this, the second largest fish in the world, are made by people in boats who sight the shark feeding in surface waters. Typically shark-shaped, it has a long snout (very long in juveniles) with the mouth on the underside of the head, a large triangular first dorsal fin, and a much smaller second dorsal fin. Apart from its enormous size, it can be recognised immediately by the five huge gill slits which extend almost all the way round the head from the back to the underside. Since it generally swims along with its mouth open, it can be seen that it has only tiny unshark-like teeth and towards the back of the mouth, a large number of long, thin, horny gill rakers, attached to the gill arches, with which it filters its planktonic food. It is a greyish brown to blackish colour, paler beneath, and often with a blotchy appearance.

SIZE: The average length around Great Britain is about 7.5m and the maximum substantiated record is 11m long. However, it can probably reach 15m and can certainly weigh over 3 tons.

162

DISTRIBUTION AND HABITAT: Basking sharks can be seen all round Great Britain and Ireland, on or near the surface. Most sightings are in the summer during calm sunny weather – hence the common name. They will approach quite close to the shore, but can also be found far out to sea. In winter, they move into deeper water and "hibernate".

BIOLOGY: The life history and biology of this harmless giant are largely unknown. They feed entirely on minute floating plants and animals (plankton), which they catch by swimming along with their huge mouths open, sieving the water through the gill rakers and out at the gill slits. At least 1500 cubic metres (nearly 330,000 gallons) of water can be filtered in this way each hour. During the winter, when little plankton is available, they shed the gill rakers, retire to deep water, and do not feed. The gill rakers are re-grown the following spring. Virtually nothing is known of their breeding habits, but they are thought to bear one, or possibly two, live young after a gestation period which may be as long as 3.5 years. Recent research indicates that distinct populations probably remain in particular areas. This, and the slow reproductive rate, makes them vulnerable to over-exploitation. In European waters fisheries for them are un-regulated, and are expanding in some areas. Markets are developing for the fins and meat as well as the traditionally-used oil-rich liver. The current population status is largely unestimated, and all sightings are valuable and should be sent to: Marine Conservation Society, 4 Gloucester Road, Ross-on-Wye, HR9 5BU.

BEHAVIOUR: Around Britain, basking sharks are usually seen singly, but they sometimes gather in large shoals. They are slow moving and ponderous, and it can be a fascinating, if awesome experience, to drop into the water nearby and swim with these huge fish.

SIMILAR SPECIES: None in British waters.

KEY IDENTIFICATION FEATURES:

1. Shark-like appearance.

2. Five very large gill slits.

3. Long snout especially in
   young.

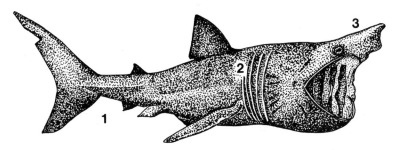

BASS

Dicentrachus labrax
(= Morone labrax)

DESCRIPTION: The bass is a very well-known fish to sea-anglers, and is probably the leading salt-water sport fish. However, it is much less often seen by divers under water. It is a brilliantly silver, thick-bodied but streamlined fish, with a greenish-grey back and a dark patch on the gill covers. It has two similarly-sized dorsal fins, set close together, the first of which is sharply spiny. A close look – rarely attained by divers – will show more spines on the lower edges of the gill covers. Young fish up to about 10cm long often have black spots on the back and sides.

SIZE: Large bass can reach 1m, long but 60cm (arm's length) is more usual. The record catch in British waters weighed 8.3kg (nearly 18.5lbs), and was taken off Eddystone lighthouse in 1975.

DISTRIBUTION AND HABITAT: Although bass can be found all round Britain and Ireland, they are essentially a warm-water species, and in summer are found mostly on the south coast, up the west coast as far as Cumbria, and in the Thames estuary. In autumn, fish in British waters migrate to warmer wintering areas, mostly off western Cornwall. Although found at all depths from the surface to 100m, bass live mostly inshore, especially around rocky reefs. They will also enter estuaries in search of food, and young fish spend their first few years here.

164

BIOLOGY: Spawning takes place close inshore, mostly in May and June, the females taking several days to lay their floating eggs. These hatch after a few days, and the fry mostly move into the shelter of estuaries and creeks, where they spend several years. After this they gradually move out into coastal waters. Around Britain the weather affects breeding success, which may be very poor in cool unsettled summers. Growth is slow, especially in British waters, and the fish live for at least 20 years. They are highly predatory adults, feeding mostly on small schooling fish such as sand eels, sprats, herring and pilchards, but they will take almost anything that moves, including fishermen's lures. The young rely initially on small crustaceans such as shrimps and crabs. In winter, feeding more or less stops. Their slow growth and slow maturation makes the bass particularly vulnerable to over-exploitation, both by anglers and commercial fishermen. Much like the salmon, it is currently a valuable and sought-after fish. The use of extremely efficient, nearly invisible, nylon gill nets poses a serious threat (and is also a constant danger to swimmers and divers), and the number of sea-anglers has also increased dramatically over the past 20 years or so. To try to alleviate the problem, there is now a minimum size limit of 35cm (14in) for taking bass.

BEHAVIOUR: Very large bass are often solitary, and divers have reported seeing the same fish in particular localities over several months. Large schools of bass voraciously attacking other fish have also been observed. Bass can move extremely fast, and are generally difficult to approach and photograph. They can sometimes be attracted by glinting objects, and young fish engrossed in feeding amongst seaweed might be stealthily approached.

SIMILAR SPECIES: At first glance, bass might be confused with grey mullet, but the latter, though found in somewhat similar habitats, has distinctly striped sides, and a much smaller head and mouth.

KEY IDENTIFICATION FEATURES:

1. Two dorsal fins, the first spiny.

2. Overall silvery colour.

3. Dark patch on rear of gill cover.

4. Spines on lower edge of gill cover.

Thick-lipped grey mullet.

THICK-LIPPED GREY MULLET
Chelon labrosus (= Mugil labrosus)

GOLDEN GREY MULLET
Liza aurata (= Mugil auratus)

DESCRIPTION: Mullet can be recognised by their torpedo-shaped, striped bodies, with two widely spaced, short dorsal fins, the first made up of only 4 spines. The mouth is small, and has rather unusual, heart-shaped lips (when seen front on), with minute bristle-like teeth on the lower edge of the upper lip. The many species in this family are very difficult to tell part, especially underwater, but only 3 occur in British waters. All have large scales, and are of a similar colour, basically some shade of grey above with silvery sides, characteristically striped with grey lengthwise bands. The golden grey mullet has a conspicuous golden patch on the cheek and gill cover, and sometimes the head and front of the body have a golden sheen. However, large individuals of the other species sometimes show this sheen as well. As its name suggests, the thick-lipped grey mullet has a wide, swollen, upper lip.

SIZE: The thick-lipped grey mullet is the largest species, reaching 75cm long and a weight of about 4.5kg. The golden grey mullet reaches only about 45cm long (short arm's length).

DISTRIBUTION AND HABITAT: Only the thick-lipped grey mullet is really common, occurring all round Britain and Ireland, but with a tendency to migrate northwards in summer and retreat southward before

166

winter. The golden-grey mullet is frequent in the English Channel and around south-west coasts of the British Isles, but becomes progressively rarer further north. Mullet are active shoaling fish, found mostly in shallow coastal water, especially over organically-rich and seaweed-covered sediments. They are typically found in harbours, bays, lagoons, saltmarsh channels and estuaries, where they may even enter fresh water. Shoals are often seen swimming right at the surface of the water.

BIOLOGY: Mullet spawn in open water close inshore during the spring and summer in cooler waters such as ours. However, it is uncertain how regularly they breed around the British Isles, which is nearly at the limit of their northern distribution. The young stay close inshore, and can sometimes be found in rock pools. Mullet feed in shoals in a way quite unlike most other fish. They move along the sea-bed, feeding on the rubbish on the bottom by taking in mouthfuls of mud and algae. This is sifted through the large gills so that mostly only bits of seaweed, worms and other edible material are swallowed – along with some sand. They will also scrape and suck off the slimy algae and diatom cover found on rocks, pier pilings and on large seaweeds. Small molluscs and crustaceans are also found in this way, but they have no teeth to deal with larger animals. The stomach acts like a muscular gizzard, and the intestine is very long to cope with the rather poor diet. Feeding more or less stops in the cold of the winter. Mullet are fished commercially with traps and seine nets, and are also caught by anglers, though they do not readily take a bait.

BEHAVIOUR: Mullet occur mostly in schools, but aquarium observations have suggested that the schools may break up at night, only re-forming if the fish are startled. Night observations on this by divers would be interesting. Mullet tend to be difficult to approach under water but are rather unpredictable, and may sometimes ignore divers, especially when nosing around jetties and boats, or when on the bottom, looking for food.

SIMILAR SPECIES: Only one other mullet, the thin-lipped grey mullet (*Liza ramada*) occurs around the British Isles. This is a relatively rare, summertime visitor, though sometimes common in southern Ireland. Similar to the thick-lipped grey mullet, it has a black spot at the base of the pectoral fin and a narrow upper lip. At first glance, mullet might be confused with bass, but these have larger mouths and un-striped bodies.

KEY IDENTIFICATION FEATURES:

1. Two widely-spaced dorsal fins.

2. Striped grey body.

3. Thick upper lip (thick-lipped grey mullet).

*Horse mackerel (left) and
mackerel.*

MACKEREL *Scomber scombrus*

HORSE MACKEREL
OR SCAD *Trachurus trachurus*

DESCRIPTION: The mackerel and horse mackerel are not closely
related, but are grouped together here because of their similar shapes and
habitat. The familiar mackerel has a long, streamlined body, with a
pointed snout and a tapering tail. There are two small, well-separated
dorsal fins, and a single anal fin. The second dorsal fin and the anal fin are
followed by a series of characteristic, small finlets, and the tail is deeply
forked. The horse mackerel is similar, though less streamlined. The dorsal
fins are set close together, and the second dorsal fin and anal fin are high
at the front, and lower near the tail. Just in front of the anal fin are two
small spines. A row of characteristic bony scales runs along the lateral line.
In colour the mackerel is a brilliant, irridescent blue-green on the back,
with irregular zebra-like dark lines, and is whitish silver below. The horse
mackerel is a darker grey or bluish-green, with silver sides, and the young
are completely silver.

SIZE: The mackerel can reach a maximum of about 66cm long, but
40cm (forearm plus hand length) is now the usual maximum. The horse
mackerel reaches 50cm, but 25cm (forearm length) is more usual.

DISTRIBUTION AND HABITAT: Both species are widely
distributed, and can be found all round Britain and Ireland, swimming in
large schools in open water. The schools move close inshore in summer,
and return to deep water offshore in winter. Horse mackerel are
particularly common around shallow offshore sand banks.

168

BIOLOGY: Mackerel spawn throughout the summer, the females producing several hundred thousand floating eggs. These hatch after a few days, and the young remain near the coast until the autumn. In UK waters, the horse mackerel spawns mostly in May and June. Mackerel feed voraciously after spawning, preying mostly on schools of sprat, herring and sand eels. At this time they will snap at almost anything, making them easy to catch. They can also filter plankton through their gills. During the winter they hardly feed, spending a lot of time idly near the bottom, in deep water. Horse mackerel have a similar diet. Mackerel provide an important food supply for larger fish, such as tunnies and sharks, and for dolphins. They are an important commercial fish, and are caught in nets, traps and on lines. They are long-lived and slow growing, and have been over-exploited in many areas. The horse mackerel is of lesser importance, and most catches are made into fish meal.

BEHAVIOUR: Mackerel are very fast swimmers, and are constantly on the move. Consequently, they are rarely seen under water by divers. Young horse mackerel are more often seen close inshore, and the juveniles are often seen in small shoals sheltering amongst the tentacles of stinging jellyfish. This association also occurs in other species (see whiting).

SIMILAR SPECIES: The spanish or chub mackerel (*Scomber japonicus = S.colias*) and the frigate mackerel (*Auxis rochei = A.thazard*) closely resemble the mackerel, but do not have such distinctive markings. They are both rare visitors to southern Britain and Ireland.

KEY IDENTIFICATION FEATURES:

1. Zebra-stripes along the back (mackerel).

2. Bony scales on lateral line (horse mackerel).

3. Finlets in front of tail (mackerel).

4. Dorsal fins widely spaced (mackerel).

5. Dorsal fins set close together (horse mackerel).

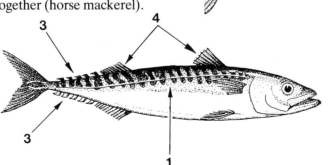

HERRING $\qquad$ *Clupea harengus*

DESCRIPTION: Members of the herring family (Clupeidae) – which includes the sprat, pilchard and shads – are all rather similar, slender, silvery fish. All have a single, short dorsal fin, a distinctly forked tail, and no lateral line. Under water they are not always easy to tell apart, unless a really close view can be obtained. The herring is flattened from side to side, but has a rounded belly, with no keel-like edge such as is found in sprat and shads. The scales are large and obvious, and come off very easily when the fish is caught or handled. A useful identification feature is that the start or origin of the dorsal fin is just above or in front of the start of the pelvic fin on the belly (this may be difficult to see in the field). The colour is silvery overall, with deep blue shading to paler blue on the back and sides. In life, there are often beautiful tints of rose-pink and gold on the sides and head.

SIZE: The size varies between races, but the maximum is about 40cm (hand plus forearm length).

170

DISTRIBUTION AND HABITAT: Herring are an abundant and widely-distributed fish, and can be found all round Britain and Ireland. There are many distinct breeding stocks or races, most of which are migratory to a greater or lesser extent. Herring live mostly in shoals, which may reach huge sizes, and which live in depths down to about 250m. Schools of young fish are found close inshore and in estuaries.

BIOLOGY: The herring was, and to a great extent still is, a very important commercial fish. The times and places of spawning vary according to the race, and there are at least 50 spawning grounds in the North Sea alone. Spring spawners tend to use spawning grounds close inshore, whilst autumn and winter spawners move offshore and onto the edges of ocean banks. In all cases the eggs are laid close to the bottom, sink down, and stick to gravel, shells and stones, forming a mat. Each female produces up to 50,000 eggs, necessary to compensate for the huge numbers eaten by fish such as haddock. The larval fish are pelagic, and drift with the currents. When about 5cm long, they gather into shoals and move into shallow water and estuaries, remaining there for 6 months to a year. These shoals, often mixed in with young sprat, are the "whitebait" so favoured by restaurants. The large Norwegian herring lives for up to 20 years; smaller races live for a shorter time, but mature earlier. Most of the known stocks migrate quite long distances from spawning and overwintering grounds to feeding grounds and back. Such movements often cause fishing disputes between different countries. Heavy overfishing in the 1950s led to a drastic decline in herring stocks, but with fishing controls these have now recovered somewhat, and the herring remains a valuable and important food fish. It is also important to predators such as sea birds, dolphins and other larger fish. Adult herring feed by sight on animal plankton, mostly copepods and euphausians (small shrimp-like crustaceans), pteropods (floating molluscs) and sand eel larvae.

BEHAVIOUR: Herring are not often seen by divers, mostly because they are an open-water species, and particularly because they tend to spend the day in deeper water coming to the surface at night. The shoals of young in inshore waters are the most likely to be seen.

SIMILAR SPECIES: Sprat, pilchard and shads are all similar. Sprat and shads have a sharp keel along the belly. Pilchard and shads have ridges on the gill covers. To add to the confusion, young herring often have a slight keel along the belly, which flattens out as they grow.

KEY IDENTIFICATION FEATURES:

1. Single dorsal fin in middle of back.

2. Rounded belly (no keel).

3. Smooth gill covers (not ridged).

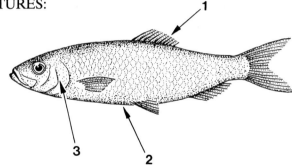

Section IV. Rarely seen fish

THIS SECTION is called "rarely seen" fish and not "rare" fish because only some of the species are genuinely rare. Others are just not encountered very often for a variety of reasons. There are obviously numerous species that could have been included in this category. Those chosen are the ones most often reported by divers and others and are relatively easy to identify.

Fish such as the undulate ray, wolf fish and garfish are not rare, but live in places where they are not very likely to be seen, such as deep water (undulate ray, wolf fish) or the surface of the open ocean (garfish). Many species, including the monkfish, stingray, eagle ray and electric ray, have their main distribution to the south in the warmer waters of the Mediterranean. They are mostly summertime visitors to our coasts, and often do not breed successfully in our cooler waters, although they may be locally common at certain times.

The black face blenny, red-mouth goby and giant goby seem to be genuinely rare. However, in the past, some species such as the leopard spotted goby, were thought to be rare, but when divers started recording them, it was found that they had simply been overlooked because of their small size and the rather inaccessible places in which they live. Thus, with careful observation, new populations of "rare" species or even new species may be discovered.

WOLF-FISH or CATFISH
Anarhichas lupus

DESCRIPTION: Anyone who meets this large and ferocious-looking fish is unlikely to forget it or to mistake it for anything else. In shape it is rather like a gigantic blenny with a long body, single long dorsal and anal fins, but no pelvic fins. The head is huge, with strong, canine-like teeth in the front of the jaws, which usually show, even when the fish is quietly resting. Its skin is tough, leathery and wrinkled, and is usually a brownish to greyish colour, with a series of darker vertical bands on the back and sides which extend up onto the dorsal fin.

174

SIZE: Adults can grow to over a metre in length.

DISTRIBUTION AND HABITAT: Wolf-fish can be found all round Great Britain and Ireland, but live mostly below about 60m down to 300m, and so are not often seen by divers. Near St. Abbs, on the Scottish east coast, they have been found in only 12m or so of water, living in small caves in a cliff face. North of the British Isles they are regularly found in shallow water. They prefer rocky areas and hard bottoms, but can also be found on mud.

BIOLOGY: The fish spawn in the winter, the females laying many thousand yellowish eggs in round ball-like clumps on the sea-bed amongst seaweeds and stones. When the eggs hatch after about two months, the larval fish stay on the bottom until their reserve of egg yolk is used up and then float freely in the plankton for a short while. By autumn they once more settle on the bottom. Wolf-fish feed on hard-shelled bottom-living animals such as crabs, sea-urchins, mussels, whelks and other shellfish, which they are easily able to crush with their powerful teeth. Worn teeth are replaced each year by new ones growing up from behind. In spite of their gruesome appearance, these fish are edible. They are caught by anglers and also, incidentally, in trawls and seine nets.

BEHAVIOUR: Wolf-fish are not overtly aggressive, and will only attack if provoked. One diver who was bitten on the arm had actually landed on the fish during his descent! Those at St. Abbs can be enticed out of their holes and hand fed.

SIMILAR SPECIES: None in British waters.

KEY IDENTIFICATION FEATURES:

1. Massive head with
   projecting teeth.

2. Long body with dark
   vertical bands.

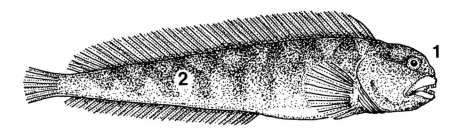

Sting ray.

STING RAY   *Dasyatis pastinaca*

EAGLE RAY   *Myliobatis aquila*

DESCRIPTION: An unexpected encounter with a stingray can prove a very painful experience. They are common in tropical waters, but perhaps luckily, only the two species featured here occur around Britain. The common sting ray is typically ray-shaped, with large, broad, wings with rounded corners, and a fairly pointed snout. The eagle ray has a very distinctive shape, with long, pointed wings – hence its name. Unlike other rays, it has a head which is clearly distinct from the rest of the disc, and has the eyes on each side. In both species the tail is long and whip-like, and has a single, long, barbed spine – the sting – set some way along the tail. Occasionally there is more than one spine. The sting ray has no dorsal fins on the tail, and the eagle ray has only one small one in front of the sting. The two species are similar in colour – usually a dark grey, olive green or brown, although some specimens are pale. The underside is whitish with grey edges.

SIZE: Most sting rays seen around Britain are less than 1m long, but they can reach 2.5m long. The eagle ray grows to 2m long.

176

DISTRIBUTION AND HABITAT: The sting ray probably occurs all round Britain and Ireland, but is noticeably more common in the south. It is really a visitor from warmer southern waters, and it is only during the summer and autumn that its numbers increase as the fish move northwards into the Channel. It lives on soft, usually sandy bottoms, and prefers calm, shallow coastal waters, including the outer parts of estuaries. Its depth limits are from about 2–70m. The eagle ray has a similar distribution but is much more rarely seen, although it can be common in the summer in the Channel and around south-west Ireland. In contrast to the sting ray, it is an active swimmer, often found near the surface, although it also lives on sand and mud down to over 100m depth.

BIOLOGY: Like the electric rays, but unlike most other rays, sting rays are live-bearers with from about 6–9 young born in each litter. Neither species breeds regularly around Britain, which is near the northern limit of their range. They feed entirely on bottom-living animals, which are dug out of the sand with the snout or the wings, which can be used to flap away the sand. The diet includes crabs, molluscs and fish, and any hard shells are crushed with their powerful, flattened teeth. The "sting", which can measure up to 13cm long, has a poison gland at its base, and can inflict an extremely painful wound. The danger to humans comes from standing on or near the ray since, it can swing the tail up and sting a leg well above any protective shoes or fins. The spine is shed periodically and a new one may grow before the old one is lost.

BEHAVIOUR: Sting rays spend much of their time lying on the sand, often partly buried. However, they can swim quite well by slowly beating their "wings" up and down. The eagle ray spends a much greater part of its time swimming on or near the surface, and with its long wings is a very graceful sight. Occasionally, they will even jump out of the water.

SIMILAR SPECIES: The tail with its long spine should serve to distinguish these two rays from all others found around Britain and Ireland.

KEY IDENTIFICATION FEATURES:

1. Long, whip-like tail with no (sting ray) or only one (eagle ray) dorsal fin.

2. Long barbed poison spine on tail.

3. Long pointed wings (eagle ray).

4. Distinct head (eagle ray).

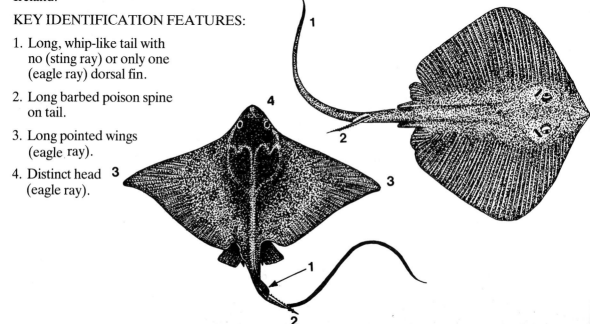

Marbled electric ray.

MARBLED ELECTRIC RAY
Torpedo marmorata

ELECTRIC RAY   *Torpedo nobiliana*

DESCRIPTION: Recognition of these fascinating fish may be important, since a shock from a large specimen can stun a grown man. Electric rays are related to the true rays and skates (Rajidae) but belong to a different family (Torpedinidae). They can easily be recognised by their rounded, disc-like body, and thick, fleshy tail, which has a well-developed tail fin. There are two small dorsal fins, set close together on the tail. These are nearly equal in size in the marbled electric ray, but the first is distinctly larger than the second in the electric ray. The skin is smooth, with no spines or scales. The two species can generally be distinguished by their colouration. As its name suggests, the marbled electric ray has a pattern of darker marbling all over its brown back. The electric ray is a uniform dark grey, deep brown or black. Both species are creamy or white on the underside. At close quarters it can also be seen that the pair of small breathing holes or spiracles behind the eyes are edged with small lobes in the marbled electric ray, but not in the electric ray.

178

SIZE: The marbled electric ray is the smaller species, reaching a length of about 60cm (arm length). The electric ray reaches over twice this, and can be nearly 2m long (180cm maximum).

DISTRIBUTION AND HABITAT: The electric ray is the commoner of the two species, and can be found all round Great Britain and Ireland as far north as the Orkneys. However, its distribution is mostly up the west coast and in the Channel. The marbled electric ray has only been recorded from southern Britain and Ireland, with most sightings in the western Channel and the southern North Sea. However, recent sightings of this species seem to be on the increase. Both species occur as shallow as 10m on sand and mud, the marbled electric ray preferring the former. The electric ray has been recorded as deep as 350m.

BIOLOGY: Unlike most other rays and skates, which lay distinctive egg cases, electric rays give birth to live young, but neither species seems to breed regularly in British waters. There is probably a northward migration from the Mediterranean each year. The diet has not been well studied, but is known to include a variety of bottom-living fish such as rockling, whiting and dogfish. The prey fish are stunned or killed by a powerful electric shock from two electric organs situated on either side of the head in the "wings", which are used to envelop the prey. The electrical discharge is believed to be a reflex action stimulated by touch, and since a large electric ray can deliver a shock of up to 220 volts at 8 amps, they should be left severely alone! The discharges occur in short bursts, and weaken the "battery", which takes some time to recharge. Fishermen have been known to receive a shock from their line even before seeing what they have hooked!

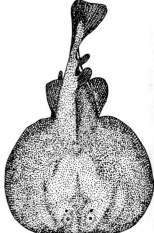

BEHAVIOUR: Both species are solitary and nocturnal. During the day they mostly lie buried in the sand, with only the eyes and spiracles showing.

SIMILAR SPECIES: None in British waters.

KEY IDENTIFICATION FEATURES:

1. Nearly circular body.

2. Large tail fin.

3. Marbled pattern
   (*T.marmorata*)

4. Uniform dark colour
   (*T.nobiliana*)

5. Lobes around spiracles
   (*T.marmorata*)

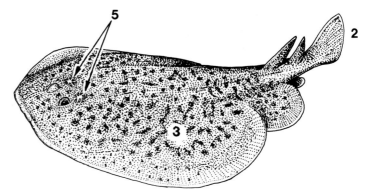

GARFISH   *Belone belone*

DESCRIPTION: With its cigar-shaped body and unusual, long, beak-like jaws, the garfish is easy to recognise. The jaws are full of sharply-pointed teeth, and in younger fish the lower jaw is distinctly longer than the upper. There is a single dorsal fin, and a single anal fin, both set well back towards the tail. Close up, it can be seen that the lateral line runs very close to the belly, rather than along the flanks, as in most fish. In the water the fish appear predominantly silver, but as with many oceanic fish, the back is a dark blue to green, and only the sides and belly are a beautiful, burnished silver. This sort of colouration provides camouflage both from above and from below in open water. Another interesting feature only likely to be noticed by fishermen and gourmets is that this fish has a distinctly green skeleton.

SIZE: Adults can reach nearly a metre long.

DISTRIBUTION AND HABITAT: The garfish inhabits the open ocean, and can be found living in the surface waters all round Britain and Ireland. In winter it lives mostly offshore, out in the eastern Atlantic, but in summer it moves into shallow coastal waters. At this time it can often be seen swimming in small shoals just beneath the surface.

180

BIOLOGY: The main spawning period is in the spring (May and June) when the females lay from a thousand to many thousand eggs. The eggs are covered in long, sticky threads, which catch in seaweed, floating debris or amongst rocks, thus partly anchoring the eggs. The young hatch out after about 5 weeks, and initially stay close inshore. At first they have short jaws, but soon, the lower jaw starts to grow and becomes much longer than the upper. However, the latter eventually catches up, and older fish have almost equal jaws. They can live for at least 18 years. Garfish feed mainly on small fish such as sand eels, young herring and sprats, which they hunt mainly by sight. This is why they are so often caught by those fishing for mackerel with a moving bait. Young fish feed initially on small crustaceans. Garfish make good eating, but people are often put off by the green skeleton and greenish flesh.

BEHAVIOUR: Garfish are shy, and not easily approached, and probably regard divers and swimmers as potential predators. They are very agile, and can sometimes be seen leaping clear of the water when being chased by tunny fish, dolphins, or other predators. They will often do the same thing when hooked by a fisherman.

SIMILAR SPECIES: The skipper (*Scomberesox saurus*) is very similar to the garfish, but only reaches about half its size. It is mainly an open-ocean species, but does come close inshore. It can be distinguished from the garfish by a row of small finlets behind both the dorsal and anal fins.

KEY IDENTIFICATION FEATURES:

1. Long, thin body.

2. Long, beak-like jaws.

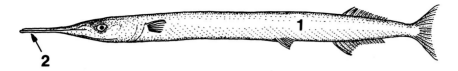

Red-mouth goby (left) and giant goby.

RED-MOUTH GOBY   *Gobius cruentatus*

GIANT GOBY   *Gobius cobitis*

DESCRIPTION: These two gobies have little in common, except that they are both large, and are both very rare around Britain and Ireland. They share the usual goby characteristics of a broad head with large eyes on top, thick lips, and puffed-out cheeks, two dorsal fins, one anal fin and a large, rounded tail fin. The red-mouth goby lives up to its name, and is easily recognised from the vivid red markings on the lips and cheeks. Its body is a warm reddish-brown, with lighter and darker blotches. At close quarters, black lines of sensory papillae can be seen on the head. The giant goby is very large and thick-set, with a chunky appearance. It is a very speckled, pale brownish to olive colour, with a lot of darker mottling and darker blotches, especially in younger fish. The darkish fins have narrow, pale edges (dorsal, anal and tail fins). Size, habitat and distribution are also helpful in identification.

SIZE: The red-mouth goby reaches 18cm long (hand size). The giant goby is the largest goby in European waters, and can reach 27cm long (forearm length).

DISTRIBUTION AND HABITAT: The red-mouth goby is very rare around Britain and Ireland, and has so far only been recorded from a few sites in southern Ireland. These include the National Nature Reserve of Lough Ine, Co. Cork, where it lives amongst rocks and sand, where there are plenty of hidey holes. In the Mediterranean it is also found in seagrass beds. The giant goby has so far only been recorded from the south-west corner of England. Here it appears to be confined to rocky shore pools

182

above about mid-tide level, often in brackish water. These pools are mostly rather bare, but with growths of green, filamentous seaweed. In the Mediterranean it lives in shallow water on rocky and weedy ground. Any information about sightings of these two species would be of interest.

BIOLOGY: Little is known of the biology of these two species. The giant goby is known to feed on green, filamentous seaweed, and crustaceans such as sand hoppers and shore crabs, all common in the pools in which they live.

BEHAVIOUR: No specific information available.

SIMILAR SPECIES: Small specimens of the giant goby might be confused with the rock goby (*Gobius paganellus*). However, this has a distinct, pale to orange band on the edge of the first dorsal fin only. A third rare species found on the shore and in shallow water is Couch's goby (*Gobius couchi*). This has so far only been recorded from Helford in Cornwall and Lough Ine, Co. Cork, but new localities are turning up. It reaches only 8cm in length; and is more likely to be confused with the black goby (*Gobius niger*).

KEY IDENTIFICATION FEATURES:

1. Bright red on lips and cheeks (red-mouth).

2. Thin, black lines on head (red-mouth).

3. Speckled, blotchy colour (giant).

4. Large size.

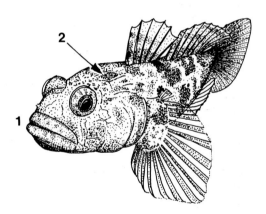

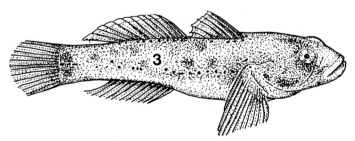

BLACK-FACE BLENNY
Tripterygion atlanticus

DESCRIPTION: With its thick lips, bulging eyes and small pelvic fins, this charming little fish resembles the true blennies (Blenniidae). It is, however, a member of the three-fin blennies (Tripterygiidae) all of which have three dorsal fins in place of the single, long one of ordinary blennies.

184

Another difference is that it has scales, whereas the blennies have slippery, scaleless skins. Males can easily be recognised by their colour alone, especially in the breeding season, when they have very black heads, and deep yellow or orange bodies. Females are a less colourful, mottled pale brown, with five oblique darker bars running across the sides.

SIZE: Adults reach about 7cm (finger size).

DISTRIBUTION AND HABITAT: So far this little fish has only been positively identified from the English Channel, in particular around Portland, where they are regularly seen by divers. Further afield, they have been tentatively identified from the northern Spanish Atlantic coast and the Channel Isles. It lives in rocky areas, hiding in crevices, in wrecks and amongst seaweeds. It has been found from the lower shore down to about 20m.

BIOLOGY: Little is yet known of the biology of this rare fish, which was first found in 1972, and described in the literature in 1975. It is very similar in appearance to the related Mediterranean black-faced blenny (*Tripterygion tripteronotus*), and probably has similar habits. The latter breed in early summer, and the males defend a small territory, enticing females in to spawn with them.

BEHAVIOUR: As yet, no specific observations have been made.

SIMILAR SPECIES: None in British waters.

KEY IDENTIFICATION FEATURES:

1. Three dorsal fins, one anal fin.

2. Small pelvic fins, with two rays.

3. Males with black head.

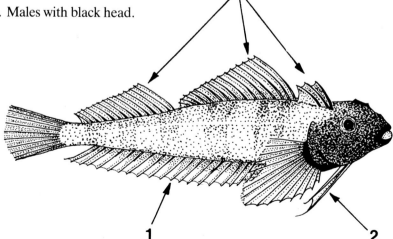

UNDULATE RAY or PAINTED RAY
Raja undulata

DESCRIPTION: This is a very distinctive ray, that can immediately be recognised from its colour pattern alone. The upper surface can be various shades of brown, but always has long, dark, wavy lines, each one edged with rows of small white spots. It has rounded wings, a very short snout, and spines on the tail, along the middle of the body, and around the eyes. There are also one or two spines between the two small dorsal fins on the tail.

SIZE: Around Britain and Ireland, this ray reaches about 1m long, but it grows bigger than this in the Mediterranean.

DISTRIBUTION AND HABITAT: Predominantly a southern species, the undulate ray can be found throughout the English Channel, and around south-west England and southern Ireland. It lives on sandy bottoms down to about 200m. It is not really rare, but is rarely seen, because although it comes into shallow water, it prefers depths below 45m.

186

BIOLOGY: The biology of this beautiful ray is little known, partly because it is of no commercial importance. Large, opaque, reddish-brown egg capsules are laid in the summer (earlier in the Mediterranean). These are 8–9cm long (excluding the horns at the corners) and are covered in fibres on one side. The diet includes plaice, dab, gobies, squids, crustaceans and other bottom-living animals.

BEHAVIOUR: No specific information is available.

SIMILAR SPECIES: There should be no confusion over this species but one other species, the small-eyed ray, also sometimes called the painted ray (*Raja microcellata*), has wavy streaks and blotches on the back. However, these are pale cream, and are not edged with white dots.

KEY IDENTIFICATION FEATURES:

1. Wavy, dark lines, edged
     with white spots.

2. Rounded wings.

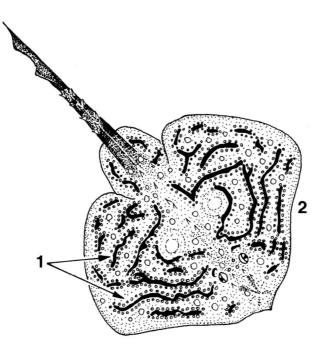

Bibliography

THERE is a large literature available on the identification, classification, history and biology of fishes. Much of this is rather specialised, but I have listed below a small number of books that I have found particularly useful in pursuing my interest in fishes and other references mentioned in the text.

Bone, Q. and Marshall, N.B. Biology of Fishes. Tertiary Level Biology. Blackie and Son Ltd. 1982.

Dipper, F.A. and Powell, A. Field Guide to the Water Life of Britain. Reader's Digest Nature Lover's Library. Reader's Digest Association Ltd., London, 1984.

Lythgoe, J. and Lythgoe, G. Fishes of the Sea. The coastal waters of the British Isles, Northern Europe and the Mediterranean. A photographic guide in colour. Blandford Press Ltd., London, 1971.

McDonald, K. Fish Watching and Photography. John Murray (Publishers) Ltd., London, 1972.

Muus, B.J. and Dahlstrøm, P. Guide to the Sea Fishes of Britain and North-western Europe. Collins, 1974.

Norman, J.R. A History of Fishes. Third edition by P.H. Greenwood. Ernest Benn Ltd., London, 1975.

Wheeler, A. Key to the Fishes of Northern Europe. A guide to the identification of more than 350 species. Frederick Warne (Publishers) Ltd., London, 1978.

Wyche, C.J. Observations on the behaviour of saithe (*Pollachius virens*) school on a temperate reef. Progress in Underwater Science, vol. 9. New Series of the Report of the Underwater Association, 1984.

Index

* Asterisk indicates species mentioned BUT not covered in full in the book.

191

PHOTOGRAPHIC CREDITS AND DETALS: BRILL. Colin Gray. Chesil Cove, Portland, 15m depth. TURBOT. Geoff Potts. Plymouth. July 1969. PLAICE. Bernard Picton. Malin Beg harbour, Co. Donegal. FLOUNDER. Seaphot. DAB. Bernard Picton. Catalina wreck, Millport, 20m. 1981. LEMON SOLE. Jim Greenfield. St. Abbs, Berwickshire. Nikonos II and close-up lens. SOLE. Elizabeth Wood. Abbot's Cliff, Kent. 4m. June 1986. ROKER. Colin Gray. Prawle Point, Devon. 15m. Nikonos and Novatek 20mm lens. CUCKOO RAY. Peter Nutton. Achmelvic point, Sutherland. 20m. July 1982 Pentax Spotmatic in housing. ANGLER FISH. Roy Waller. Eyemouth, Berwickshire. July 1983 Nikonos III and close up lens. COMMON DOGFISH. Elizabeth Wood. Plymouth Sound. 10m. May 1986. Nikon F and macro lens. NURSEHOUND. Andy Purcell. Aberaeron, Dyfed. 10m. July 1984. Nikon F3 and 55m lens. SMOOTH HOUND. David George. SPURDOG. Rico Oldfield. TOPE. D. Nicholson. TUB GURNARD. Seaphot. RED GURNARD. Mark Deeble and Victoria Stone. GREY GURNARD. Bernard Picton. Howton Head, Orkney, August 1979. POGGE. Jim Greenfield. COMMON DRAGONET (female). Jo Jamieson. Brixham, Devon. Shallow. Nikonos III and close up lens. COMMON DRAGONET (male). David George. RED MULLET. Jim Greenfield. Plymouth Sound. Nikon F3 plus macro lens. BLACK GOBY. Bernard Picton. Salt Lake. Clifden, Co. Galway. PAINTED GOBY. Jo Jamieson. Millport. Shallow. August 1981. 1:2. SAND GOBY. Jim Greenfield. Plymouth Sound. Nikon F3 and macro lens. BUTTERFLY BLENNY. Mark Deeble and Victoria Stone. VIVIPAROUS BLENNY. Seaphot. GREATER PIPEFISH. Jo Jamieson. Chesil beach, Dorset. 9m. June 1983. 1:6. DEEP-SNOUTED PIPEFISH. Mark Deeble and Victoria Stone. RED BAND FISH. Chris Bridge. Aquarium photograph. Fish caught off Lundy Island. LESSER WEEVER. Seaphot. SAND EELS. Dave Peake. Polhawn Cove, Cornwall. Shallow. July 1985. SNAKE BLENNY. D. W. Connor. TOPKNOT. Roy Waller. Eyemouth, Berwickshire. July 1983. Nikonos III and close-up lens. NORWEGIAN TOPKNOT. Jim Greenfield. St. Abbs. Nikon F3 and macro lens. BLOCH'S TOPKNOT. Bernard Picton. Millport. 5m. 1981. LUMPSUCKER. Jim Greenfield. St. Abbs, Berwickshire. Nikon F3 and macro lens. MONTAGU'S SEA SNAIL. Seaphot. SHORE CLINGFISH. W. Williams. CONNEMARA CLINGFISH. Bernard Picton. Lough Ine, Co. Cork. August 1980. TWO SPOTTED CLINGFISH. Frances Dipper. LEOPARD SPOTTED GOBY. Roy Waller. Eyemouth, Berwickshire. July 1982. Nikonos II and close up lens. ROCK GOBY. Bernard Picton. Gerd's hole, Ard bay, Co. Galway. April 1982. TOMPOT BLENNY. John Taylor. SHANNY. Roy Waller. Eyemouth, Berwickshire. Rock pool. Nikonos and 1:3 extension tube. MONTAGU'S BLENNY. Colin Gray. Aquarium photograph. Fish caught in rock pool, Porthkerris, Cornwall. YARRELL'S BLENNY. Bernard Picton. Catalina wreck, Millport. 20m. BUTTERFISH. Jim Greenfield. St. Abbs, Berwickshire. Nikon F3 and macro lens. SEA SCORPION. Bernard Picton. St. John's point, Co. Donegal. BULL ROUT. Jim Greenfield. St. Abbs, Berwickshire. Nikon F3 and macro lens. SNAKE PIPEFISH. Linda Pitkin. WORM PIPEFISH. Rico Oldfield. CONGER EEL. Colin Gray. Portland Bill. 25m. September 1984. Canon F1 and 55m lens. EEL. Andy Purcell. Chasewater, West Midlands. 3m. Nikon F3 and 55mm lens. LING. Bernard Picton. St. John's point, Co. Dongeal. SHORE ROCKLING. Geoff Potts. Plymouth. THREE-BEARDED ROCKLING. Colin Gray. Wreck James Fennel, Portland. 16m. July 1986. Canon F1. FIVE-BEARDED ROCKLING. Andy Purcell. Aquarium photograph. Fish caught in lobster pot, Aberaeron, Dyfed. 9m. August 1986. TADPOLE FISH. Graham Ackers. FIFTEEN-SPINED STICKLEBACK. Jim Greenfield. Aquarium photograph. THREE-SPINED STICKLEBACK. Roy Waller. Eyemouth, Berwickshire. May 1986. Nikonos III and 1:3 extension tube. CUCKOO WRASSE (female). Jim Greenfield. Plymouth breakwater. Nikonos II and close-up lens. CUCKOO WRASSE (male). John Taylor. BALLAN WRASSE. Bernard Picton. GOLDSINNY WRASSE. Jim Greenfield. Plymouth breakwater. Nikonos II and close-up lens. ROCK COOK. Bernard Picton. Whirlpool cliff, Lough Ine, Co. Cork. CORKWING. Andy Purcell. Aquarium photograph. Fish caught in rock pool, Aberaeron, Dyfed. August 1986. BLACK SEA BREAM. Geoff Potts. Plymouth. TWO-SPOT GOBY. Roy Waller. St. Abbs, Berwickshire. May 1986. Nikonos III and 1:3 extension tube. JOHN DORY. Colin Gray. Cornwall, at night 15m. Canon F1. HADDOCK. Seaphot. WHITING. Andy Purcell. Mew Stone, Plymouth. 10m. August 1984. Nikon F3. POOR COD. Roy Waller. Eyemouth, Berwickshire. August 1985. Nikonos III and close-up lens. BIB. John Taylor. POLLACK. Jim Greenfield. St. Abbs, Berwickshire. SAITHE. Seaphot. BASKING SHARK. Richard Price. BASS. Colin Gray. Landing craft wreck, Chesil beach. 15m. 1975. Nikonos and 35mm lens. THICK LIPPED GREY MULLET. Colin Gray. Grove point, Portland. 10m. Canon F1 and 55mm lens. MACKEREL. Geoff Potts. Aquarium photograph, Plymouth. HORSE MACKERAL. Jim Greenfield. St. Abbs, Berwickshire. Nikon F3 and macro lens. HERRING. J. King. WOLF FISH. Jim Greenfield. St. Abbs, Berwickshire. Nikon F3 and macro lens. STING RAY. Lawson Wood. MARBLED ELECTRIC RAY. Maggie Gray. Chesil Cove. 15m. June 1979. Nikonos III and 35mm lens. GARFISH. Maggie Gray. Grove. August 1981. Nikonos III and 35mm lens. RED MOUTH GOBY. Bernard Picton. Whirlpool Cliff, Lough Ine, Co. Cork. GIANT GOBY. David Lewis. BLACK FACE BLENNY. Graham Ackers. UNDULATE RAY. Colin Gray. Grove 23m. August 1986. Canon F1 and 55mm lens. COD. Jim Greenfield.

194